Me, Then

Me, Then

Mia Kim

Methuen

ME, THEN

First published by Methuen in 2021

1

Methuen
Orchard House, Railway Street,
Slingsby, York YO62 4AN

Copyright © 2021 by Mia Kim

A CIP catalogue record for this book is available from
the British Library.

ISBN: 978 0 413 77841 3

Methuen Publishing Limited Reg. No. 3543167

Typeset by SX Composing DTP, Rayleigh, Essex
Printed and bound in Great Britain by
CPI Group (UK) Ltd, Croydon, CR0 4YY

www.methuen.co.uk

To Robert,
my oasis

Acknowledgements

Thank you, Robert McKee, for walking with me through the world of Su-young.

I am grateful to Peter Tummons, my publisher at Methuen, for his insight and guidance. You have the lightest of touch.

The wise readers of Sherman Library Book Club: Ashleigh Blake, Catherine D'Andrea, Suzan Ashley, Pat Corrigan, Stephanie Spinner, Corrine Kervokian. Thank you for the early-draft notes.

My appreciation to Dennis Swanson for your generosity and trust; Marcia Friedman for your encouragement and expertise; Elizabeth Indianos for your passion for good stories; Christa Echtle for standing by me; Jorge Fernandez for your good cheer.

My gratitude to Brunonia Barry, Alison Noël, and Susan Orlean for your encouragements.

My heart felt thank you to Joanne Soja, Tom Mani, Doo-san Shim, Mr. and Mrs. Shim, Candace Bowes, David Kurtz, Euan Borland, Paul McKee, Carol Tambor, Steve Gottlieb, Owen Fitzpatrick.

Josie, Andrea and Patrika, my dearest sisters, you are loved.

네 엄마는 네 아잇적 그 강기슭

Your mother is the riverbank of your childhood

— Poet, Kim Hyesoon

Cruelty has a Human Heart
And Jealousy a Human Face
Terror, the Human Form Divine
And Secrecy, the Human Dress

—William Blake

Chapter One

1964. Seoul, Korea

Red drops plopped on my white shirt, little dots unfolding, expanding like the petals of a late summer's touch-me-not. I felt the wetness drip from my nose to my lips. A metallic taste. I swiped at it and gasped, less from pain than the shock of seeing blood. I'd never seen my blood before, or any blood. Just then, Mrs. Han swooped down, pulled me up by my hair, and smacked the side of my head. The force threw me against a tree—just my luck to hit the lone tree in the front yard—I bounced off it and fell forward on my face, scraping along the gravel, my chin and palm burned. I started to push myself up, only to stare at Mrs. Han's feet in front. She grabbed me once more, I crouched against her next blow, but it didn't come. From out of nowhere, Mom lunged in and blocked her fist, taking the hit herself. Mrs. Han looked stunned, me too. Mom wasn't to come for another three days.

1

Mrs. Han stammered, blurting out that I was clumsy and fell, all by myself, but before she could say more, Mom put me on her back and ran out of the house.

She fast-stepped through the narrow alleyways, my chin banging against her shoulder like a woodpecker. If I weren't piggybacked, she would've sprinted. The sharp morning sun stung the back of my neck and arms. I covered Mom's bare arms with my hands, shielding them from the sun. She asked if I could walk; I was getting too heavy and too hot. I shook my head, clinging tighter to her sweat-soaked back. With my head resting on her damp neck, smelling her hair, I'd already forgotten the beating. I was happy on her back, as if I were in her womb again—floating and safe, moving without moving.

The narrow streets on the edge of Seoul were empty except for a scrawny dog that snarled and barked, spit bubbling from his jagged teeth. Dogs were never pets, but ferocious guard dogs or feral strays. Mom marched right past him. I, normally terrified of them, stuck out my tongue, secure on her back.

Mom slowed when we turned onto a wide tree-lined boulevard. The shops were waking up: merchants cranking up their iron-rollup doors, an old man hanging up his wares on the doorframe hooks, a woman splattering her storefront with a bucket of water to settle the dust. People passed us without wasting a smile. Mom stopped in the shadow of a tall tree, catching her breath. I wanted to ask where we were going, why she came three days early, but didn't. My few clothes were still in the corner of Mrs. Han's living room; I kept quiet about that too.

Through the gnarled tree branches, Mom gazed up at the sky, her habit whenever she was thinking. I squinted up too. The sun played peekaboo, flickering between the leaves. Mom patted my bottom, rocking me side to side, reassuring me that all was well, but soon, she let out a long sigh and sank down. She sobbed. It frightened me; I'd never seen her cry. I wriggled myself down from her back and toddled around her. I was really sorry I made her sad; I wished she'd spank me if it would make her feel better. All this—her crying, our running sweaty with no place to go—was my fault, all because the night before I'd committed a crime and got caught.

Four days ago, Mom brought me to Mrs. Han who met us at her gate that opened onto a large walled-in courtyard. She beamed at me, pinched my cheek, in a friendly way, and led us across the clean-swept courtyard to an immaculate, spacious living room. Her house was a stately, traditional Korean home with a grooved slate roof that fanned upwards in the corners. As people normally did in hot weather, she had opened the living room shoji doors wide, letting the breezes through the front and back yards. Made of thin wooden lattice and covered in semi-opaque rice paper, shoji doors let the sunlight filter in, and also slid from side to side, dividing the rooms efficiently. In the front yard, the shy and modest touch-me-not plants dotted along the base of the wall; in the backyard, colourful peonies and wild roses erupted, giving a lush, gay air to this otherwise solemn and orderly house.

Mrs. Han was tall like Mom, a bit skinnier, but her mouth terrified me. It was alive all on its own. From her protruding purplish gums, pointed teeth jutted out in all directions, jam packed, each elbowing for space; when she wasn't speaking, her darting tongue licked her upper lip over and over again.

"Unni, thank you so much. I'll not forget this," Mom said, handing Mrs. Han a roll of money which she quickly dropped into her skirt pocket. "Unni" meant older sister, a term often used as a mark of respect when a younger woman addressed an older female. It also bonded them.

"Don't mention it. You are like a sister to me. If I weren't so hard up, I wouldn't take your money. Ah-gha should call me 'aunt' from now on," she said, catching my eye, smiling.

Mom swung me around onto her lap and smoothed my hair. "My little puppy, my little monkey . . . Ah-gha-ya, can you show me how many days are in a week?"

That wasn't difficult, I was almost five years old. I counted them out on my fingers.

"How smart you are." Mom patted me. "So, one finger for one day. When you've counted off seven, I'll be back. Till then, be good and obey Mrs. Han, yes?" She stood up. I tried to climb back into her arms, but

4

she held me away and dashed out of the door, out of sight. I tried to run after her, but Mrs. Han gripped my shoulders, pulling me back.

"No, you stay with me. You'll be alright here." I screeched for my Mom to come back as Mrs. Han walked to the gate and locked it.

There were no other kids in Mrs. Han's household, only seven adults. In the morning, everyone moved about frantically except her father and grandma. Mrs. Han, her three brothers and her mother all squatted in a semicircle around the water pump in the backyard, washed their faces and arms in a great rush, then trotted back to their rooms to get dressed. Soon after, all sat around the low table in the living room, ate quickly, and bolted out of the gate. Then the house stood still like a headstone in a forgotten cemetery.

All day long, grandma, who could barely see or move, sat hunched over in the corner of the living room, mending clothes and sewing on buttons with her knobbly fingers. Her small crumpled face poked out from her voluminous Korean dress. Through her huge magnifying glasses perched on her hooked nose, her unblinking, gigantic murky eyeballs peered out at me like an owl. Everywhere I turned—the walls, the closed doors, the spotless grounds—all seemed to say, "Don't touch. Stay away." So, I kept near grandma, and when she didn't shoo me away, I inched closer to her like a hesitant spider doing a sideways dance, and watched her sew.

A day frozen in time; nothing moved except for grandma's fingers and the clouds that played hide and seek with the sun, turning everything dark one minute, bright the next. From inside her rolled-up sleeve, grandma fished something out, put it on the floor and went on sewing. It was a piece of hard candy which I cautiously picked up. The wrapper was stuck tightly round the candy, so I put the whole thing in my mouth and let my saliva work its way into the wrapper; the sweetness was heavenly, the sourness made my mouth water. Grandma gazed at me, the corners of her sunken mouth upturned in a smile, her watery eyes warm.

In the centre of their generous front yard, a gorgeous almond tree towered over the house, its many zig-zagging branches heavy with clusters of white delicate blossoms spilling over the wall to the street beyond. Day and night those tender little flowers fell to the ground, swirling like baby butterflies. Mrs. Han's father swept away the fallen petals as many as three times a day, unhurriedly, with great care. He also wiped clean the outsides of a dozen or so large urns standing against the backyard's stone wall, patiently waiting for autumn when they would be filled with preserved food—a half dozen different kinds of kimchee, fermented soy beans, and hot pepper pastes—enough to last the entire winter. I wanted to help sweep and clean, even pick up some fallen petals to play with, but I didn't ask. Something told me that even the dead petals belonged to him.

Mrs. Han and her mother came back in the early evening. After changing their clothes, they went on to cleaning—no chatting, no laughter, just an obsession with their already spotless, shiny home.

The three brothers stumbled in shortly before the midnight curfew, their faces bright red from drinking, their rubbery arms and faltering steps knocking and kicking along the walls and doors, but without the loud, rough talk of drunkards.

All eight of us slept in the large living room with shoji doors wide open, the only place where the night air lazed in and out. The three brothers slept at one end, then the father, mother, and Grandma. Mrs. Han and I slept at the other end, me against the wall. As the adults slept they snored, some loudly and for long periods. Mrs. Han's throat rattled each time she inhaled; Mr. Han puffed and blew, while the others gurgled, wheezed, and whistled, loud enough to be heard above the cicadas' manic buzzing. Whenever the cicadas paused, the crickets took over. I was lost for sleep, my ears tuned to the uneven rhythms of the night's great chorus.

Laying still, I checked my to-do list. I had three things to find out: who's kind and who's not, and where to hide. So far I avoided everyone except Grandma, and I hadn't found my hiding place yet since I wasn't sure where I was allowed to go and where not; rooms were always closed shut but more out of orderliness than privacy, I thought. There was the storage space next to the outdoor kitchen where the bushels of rice and other dried goods were kept, but I ruled that out: rats ran loose there. I knew this because I'd seen them in other homes.

Before coming to Mrs. Han's, I lived with a woman who ran a food stand selling kimbap in Seoul train station. She was youngish, but bent like an old lady, walking slowly. She was gentle and soft-spoken and lived alone. Each day she got up in the black of night to make kimbap—rice, spinach, thin slices of fishcake and carrots all rolled inside a sheet of dried seaweed. She sliced each roll into bite-size pieces and arranged them in paper-thin, throwaway bamboo boxes. The delicate dried seaweed sheets tore easily, and no matter how carefully she rolled them, very often the contents spilled out. We ate the ruined pieces and the uneven ends. She then stacked the kimbap boxes on her small cart that doubled as a food stand and pulled it through the snaking sleepy streets, sometimes carrying me on her back, more often, with me walking alongside her. By the time we arrived at the train station, the sky glowed with the dawn's cool blue.

One especially hectic day while she was tending the lunchtime crowd, I wandered off, dazzled by the stands all around us selling their wares; paper fans, pillows knitted with multi-coloured plastic straws, hats woven with bamboo strands, shoes made from rubber, with their front tips painted in pink and green, makeup for the ladies, shirts, dresses—any and all things people wanted and needed before they hopped on the train. I was drawn to one special stand. It sold candies, cookies, shrimp crackers, and other snacks. I stood glued to it, staring and staring, imagining their smell, feel, taste. Before I knew it, I was on tiptoe, my fingers stroking a piece of gum, wrapped so alluringly in yellow paper and silver foil. I picked one up; it wanted to be picked up. *Wham*, a hand swatted my wrist, the gum fell back into its place and I was swooped up into the kimbap woman's arms. She was shaking and in tears, almost hysterical; she'd been searching all over for me. That was the end of my stay with her.

The nights were long in Mrs. Han's house, the nocturnal chorus of snoring and insects intense. Mostly I was too hungry to sleep, but I dared not ask for more rice. Mrs. Han's toothy smiles on that first day with Mom never came back. Now with her mouth clamped shut, she looked right past me, pointing her finger or lifting her chin up or down for me to come or go; mainly I stayed out of her way. To be fair, everyone ate sparingly: breakfast, normally the biggest meal of the day, was half a bowl of rice, kimchee, a clear broth with thin radish pieces floating on it, and a clump of sweet and salty black beans; lunch was a bowl of cold noodles mixed in hot red paste, so spicy hot it brought tears to your eyes; dinner included a piece of fish, rice and pickled cucumber slices. Mrs. Han gave me whatever was left over after serving the grownups.

On the fourth night the trouble began.

An enormous moon beamed on the sleeping bodies, bright enough for me to see a patch of black hair feathering out from Mrs. Han's underarm. As I didn't have any, I watched hers with a great curiosity. Something about it was creepy, even threatening. What if they grew and grew, spreading out, overtaking her, turning her into a black-haired monster, her face filled with gigantic jagged teeth. Don't spook yourself, I told myself, and turned away.

The moonlight also glinted on silvery fish scales from a string of fish hanging from the wall, drying, five in all, each the size of a flattened zucchini. My stomach growled. I wondered if dried fish tasted like the dried squid people ate as snacks. The more I stared, the hungrier I got. They were dangling right above me, close enough that I wouldn't even have to stand on tiptoe. I got up, tugged at the bottom one. The fish loosened from its string. I put it under my nose—my habit of smelling things before putting them in my mouth—a mild rotting odour stung my nostrils, but I convinced myself that it smelled a bit like dried squid, so it should taste like one too. I bit at the tail end where it was driest and least smelly, and holding my nose, I chewed it fast and gulped it down. But it didn't go down; instead, it got stuck at the back of my throat. I gagged and flailed, and fell right onto Mrs. Han's head. She yelped and shot up. Everyone woke up. Someone turned on the light. Someone else smacked me on the back. I coughed out the fish chunk, tears blinding me. Mrs. Han shook her head, her face furious. She shoved me back to my corner, telling everyone to go back to sleep.

Soon, the cicadas blasted again, and the rattling throats, too. I curled up, working to stop my teeth from chattering, hoping that by morning Mrs. Han would have forgotten the incident.

She hadn't. She shook me up from my sleep. As I came to, she whacked me: "You filthy runt! So little and already stealing. What a monster you'll grow to be! I will beat the thief outta you." Her mom, father, Grandma, and brothers watched silently as she grabbed a fistful of my hair and threw me against the wall.

When Mom took me away from Mrs Han's I was so glad and hoped never to see her again, but we did.

Chapter Two

Mom and I stopped in front of a small store on a wide, hectic, down-sloping street. On either side, shops stood shoulder to shoulder, almost falling over one another. One-story shops squeezed against multistory buildings. Some were old and crumbling, others gleaming, new and tall like giants among elves—harbingers of the tomorrow of Seoul and Korea. Cars, people, vendors all jostled for space. A man on a bicycle struggled to pull a large cart with crates piled on high, like an ant hauling a leaf a hundred times its size. Women carried big round bundles perfectly balanced on their heads, babies on their backs, deftly walking between the cars. A pedlar split open a watermelon from his cart, showing off its riotous red flesh and black seeds, bursting of summer. He shouted he was there only one day, but everyone knew he'd be there tomorrow and the day after tomorrow as long as the watermelon season lasted.

We were in Ah-hyun Dong, Mapo Gu, an energetic, fast growing district. It sat just above the Han River, which cut through the bottom third of Seoul.

Mom pushed the shop door in. A bell tinkled. Muggy hot air outside melded right in with the musty, stuffy air inside. An electric fan in the far corner creaked from side to side. Rolls of fabric leaned against one wall, their edges flapping madly whenever the fan turned towards them. Near the window were two sewing machines, shiny and black, their graceful necks adorned with golden letterings, their foot pedals idling below.

A middle-aged woman looked up through her round-rimmed eyeglasses. She nodded at Mom but went right back to her work, drawing white chalk lines on a dark blue fabric. Mom sat herself on a short stool, pulling her sweat-soiled blouse away from her ribs.

Soon the woman folded her work and sat down, facing Mom. My *nunchi* told me to move away, that I shouldn't listen to their talk. I had a lot of *nunchi*; it wasn't really a compliment, especially for a kid like me who had to depend on it to stay safe. *Nunchi* was a double-edged word: it meant I was smart, but it also meant I wasn't innocent, that I was too street-smart at such a young age, that rather than trusting, I measured things and people. You'd never describe a respected elder as having a lot of *nunchi*, not within his earshot anyway; instead, you'd say he was wise and insightful. I was ashamed of having *nunchi* too, whatever the amount. But I needed it. It helped me to avoid getting caught in a wrong place at a wrong time, doing the wrong things, getting in trouble. It was my survival tool, like my to-do list at Mrs. Han's. No matter, I still seemed to get into trouble.

I walked over to the window display where two mannequins stood facing the window. I'd been eyeing them, having never seen one before. They were identical, with their eyes closed with long black painted lashes and pouty red mouths. But the one on the left wore only a skirt, her nakedness exposed for all to see. Her body tilted forward, like bowing to the pedestrians outside. What I really couldn't take my eyes off was the sinister-looking gap on her backside: a long gash across her waist detached her torso from her hips, wide enough for my hand to poke through. Inside the dark and hollow torso, a thick menacing metal rod staked through the length of her body. I squeezed in on the mannequins' narrow platform; I felt the urge to touch, to do something to right her.

"Don't touch that, dangerous," Mom warned. "Ah-gha-ya, come and bow to your Aunt . . . She is my older sister. Yes, a real sister. Did you know that she raised me when I was little like you?"

Aunt gazed at me, quietly. She didn't look anything like my Mom. Mom was all curves: a round warm face, generous bosom, narrow waist, shapely legs. Aunt, all angles, someone you wanted to be careful with: cutaway cheeks, sharp straight nose, and long slanted, serious eyes behind her small glasses. Mom was loved for her smile. It started from the crinkled corners of her trusting eyes, then her plush mouth upturned into a crescent moon, deepening her dimples, her perfect, white teeth flashing. Before you knew it, the warmth of her smile flooded the room, rendering you helpless against her happiness swathing you. With Aunt, her thin lips curved upwards and that was that. But I liked the way she worked; tall and slim in a form fitting navy-blue dress, her long hands were agile and accurate, drawing, cutting, pinning and flipping the layers of fabric with a flick of her fingers. She didn't look like she ever broke sweat.

Mom took me to the wall of fabrics and parted them where there was a small door. She pushed it open to reveal a large room and told me to sit down.

"Stay here while I talk to your aunt," she said, closing the door behind her.

I laid down; my back felt good against the cold floor. One unlit light bulb dangled from the ceiling; inside its clear glass, a tiny squiggly wire shivered like a fragile living thing. Just then something lurched in my heart. I'd been afraid and angry before but now I experienced a new feeling, an uneasiness, queasiness, something like emptiness, not in my stomach but closer to my throat.

I wondered how long I'd be here this time, or whether we'd be going somewhere else. Mom always said we'd live together, and soon, but those were just words, her parting words, without a when or a how.

As long as I could remember, she came and went as I lived with various people, a week here, a month there. The hardest part was when she said goodbye; I'd get terrified, although she always came back. I knew this was our way of life until the day when Mom would be ready for me. I didn't sulk or cry much during her absence although, sometimes, I was very tearful. But as long as no one hit me and I had enough to eat, I was busy soaking in my five-year-old life.

Lying on my back, I took in the room. To my right, a large chest, the only furniture in the room, filled the entire wall. It had many drawers and cupboards and a long mirror on the right. I opened one of the bottom cupboards; except for a few stray books, it was empty so I crawled in. It smelled of aged wood and mellowed soybean wax, the linty rice paper lining was soft to the touch like the fur of a caterpillar. The space was perfect for me when I curled up. I'd found a wonderful hiding place and, I thought, I just might like living in this house.

When I crawled out of the stuffy cupboard, the harsh sunlight streaming through the open shoji door on my right blinded me. Just then a huge moon face appeared, beaming at me. The face belonged to a large young woman. She came towards me, cooing, her arms flung wide open, her ample bosom bouncing up and down. I put up my hands in protest. She wasn't frightening, nothing like Mrs. Han, but I didn't want to be hugged. She wasn't my Mom.

"And who might you be?" the grinning face asked, and without waiting for my answer, she rambled on in a sing-song voice: "How adorable! Oh, but what happened to your knees and your chin? Why is there blood on your shirt? Did you fall? Get into a fight? What's your name, little girl? You hungry? How about a rice cake? Some melon? Wait here, I'll come right back." Out she went before I'd said a word, her plump thighs swooshing against each other through her tight chequered pants.

The shoji door opened onto a drowsy, sun-doused yard. Although shabby and tiny compared to Mrs. Han's home, the dirt ground was well-swept with a tall water pump in the middle on a small square of cement. No trees or shrubbery anywhere. Looking out from the room, I saw that the house surrounded the water pump on three sides: to the left was the kitchen; in front, beyond the water pump, was another room; to the right was the back of a neighbour's house; and behind that, were the roofs of other neighbouring houses. I felt movements and sounds all around—kids hollering, moms yelling, pots clanging, cars honking. A rush of excitement ran through me. I sprang up, eager to go out and explore, when bang, someone ran into me and I fell back. Looking up I saw a girl my age. She was scrawny, smelling of outdoors and sweat, a loose ponytail barely holding her dishevelled hair. Mostly, she was filthy. Dirt speckled her runny nose, her grimy feet left marks on the clean soybean-waxed floor. We both stared, sizing each other up. I sat up tall, feeling superior. I was soiled too, but I had good reason; I was sure she didn't have to get rescued from scary Mrs. Han.

The girl plopped down on the floor with her grubby knees wide apart. From her pocket, along with more dirt, she took out five stones the size of her thumb. She gathered them up in one pile and picked a stone from it; she threw it straight up in the air, and while that was in the air, she grabbed the other four stones and quickly turned her wrist over; the stone in the air landed neatly in her hand, with the other four. I was amazed and impressed. She grinned and then did it again. Another success.

"I bet you can't do it," she said.

"Yes I can."

"No, you can't," she shot back.

I grabbed at her stones but she cupped them in her hand, jabbing me with her elbow. I shoved her and she fell back, I snagged a stone. She pulled me away, grabbing the back of my shirt, going for other stones. Soon we were wrestling on the floor, I got on top of her, prying her clamped fingers open. She yelped and released the stones. We both scurried after them.

"Stop. Both of you!" Aunt shouted. "How many times do I have to tell you not to bring them into the house! You will scratch the floor. Will you ever listen!" Her hand rose up to strike the girl. The girl quickly pointed her finger at me and shouted: "She made me do it!"

That was my first encounter with In-sook, my cousin, older than me by a year. From that day on, we played together, fought each other, often viciously, and ate and slept together.

I had two other cousins: Kang-jin, the oldest, seventeen, whom I called "Oppa," meaning older brother, and Mi-hae, sixteen, whom I called "Unni," older sister. Although In-sook was a year older than me, we called each other by name. Aunt's husband also lived with us, whenever he came home from his travels. I simply called him "Uncle," and Aunt, just "Aunt." The chubby, chatty young woman, Lee, was an all purpose helper: the housekeeper at home and Aunt's assistant at her shop. People called me Ah-gha. I was now living in a house bustling with people.

Chapter Three

Living with Aunt meant observing a strict routine. Each morning before dawn, no matter the weather, Aunt and Lee squatted by the water pump and washed themselves. We all washed out in the yard, two at a time as the cemented area around the pump was small. Although it was mid-spring, snow had dusted everything overnight. On a chilly day like this, Aunt and Lee added a bit of precious hot water from the kitchen into their basins. Kang-jin washed next, by himself, then Mi-hae. The two of them used up all the hot water Lee could spare from her cooking, leaving In-sook and me only frigid water. We didn't complain as we were taught to respect our older siblings just as we'd do our parents. So we just flicked our fingers in the icy water, squealing and carrying on, pretending to wash.

Squatting next to us, Lee shot In-sook a mean look, scrubbing the urine stains out of her bottom blanket. In-sook bed wetted. Aunt said it was because she was still the baby in the family. Then she'd knuckle In-sook's forehead, giving her an earful, "Aigoo, you'll be a first grader soon and still wetting. Aren't you embarrassed? Next time, I'll make you wash out your own pee, Lee has enough to do without your nonsense." But, no matter the scolding, In-sook wet her bed, and laughing, she'd run off in her stinky pants. I didn't bed wet. Mom said she didn't have to potty train me, either. Although I don't remember that far back, after hearing it over and over, I became convinced that I was an extra-ordinarily neat and tidy person.

At the beginning of winter, Uncle bound the water pump with cloths and thick straw-ropes to keep it from freezing. But as deep winter settled in, layers of sleek icicles formed around it like a fortress, water inside frozen solid. Then, slowly and carefully, Lee poured a jug of hot water all over it, as we all watched with great suspense: will it thaw or burst. More often than not, once frozen, it was useless; we had to wait until it got warmer to do the hot water treatment again. Till then, we resorted to using the emergency water stored in two big clay urns in the kitchen. When that ran out, we went to the neighbours, hoping they had some to spare.

We were told never to force the water pump handle in the middle of winter. If it didn't give, not even a little jiggle, leave it as is and alert Aunt or Lee right away, we were warned. If you forced it, the frozen, thin plunger would break off, then you've got a huge mess. No water for an entire winter. Even worse, it could be ten stinging lashes from Aunt for being careless.

After her morning wash, Aunt went to Si-jang, the open-air market, down the main street to buy fresh vegetables, fish, or meat for that day's meals. We didn't own a refrigerator or a freezer. No one did, no one knew such things existed.

Except for the curfew from midnight to 4.00 am, Si-jang never rested. The vendors repeated their daily ritual of setting up and striking the stalls and tents, competing for and battling with customers; every mother and housekeeper thought herself a master haggler. Aunt was no exception. On rare times when she had to make an extra trip to Si-jang later in the day, she would let us come with her, which was a real treat as it meant she'd buy us sweets, and we got to watch her charming, arguing, even bullying the vendors into giving her what she wanted. We felt safe and proud to belong to her.

In-sook and I didn't go to kindergarten; our district didn't have one. The idea of kindergarten was still new and considered a luxury. Instead, we played. As long as we came back for lunch and dinner, Aunt never asked what we did out of doors. Our playground was wherever we happened to be—the winding back alleyways, the main street where Aunt's shop was situated, or all the way down to Si-jang. We'd squat and watch the water tanks of eels gliding and looping in and around each other, so packed that at first glance, they looked like tanks full of thick, black churning oil. Or we'd gaze at shrimps and crabs clawing on top of one another as if trying to escape. We taunted each other to grab at a crab, daring to get our fingers nipped by its razor-sharp pincers. We choked at but were fascinated by the mounds of fish innards strewn on the wet dirt, at the powerful stinging odour of fermented soybean pastes and blocks, and urn after urn of dozens of different kinds of kimchee. We salivated over vegetable pancakes sizzling in pork fat; heaps of savoury, roasted silkworm pupae with bodies that expanded like accordions when we pulled at the ends; and the rice cakes, so moist and chewy, dusted in sweet soybean powder. We revelled in the colourful, stinky, noisy, cramped, vibrant Si-jang, thriving with life.

Also there was an abandoned plot at the end of our narrow, winding back road where we plucked off acacia blossoms for their sweet nectar. Eventually, a Methodist church took that land and added a playground for their Sunday school kids. For us it was an incredible coup. It had a set of swings, seesaws, climbing metal bars and even a merry-go-round. The church didn't seem to mind when the neighbourhood kids played there. On any given day there would be a half dozen of us, ready for anything. We took games and winning seriously. For seesawing, we stood up on the board, sitting was for sissies, and dared each other to leap higher. I practiced over and over again for the sweetest landing spot, so that on the rebound I would soar so high that for a few seconds I'd be suspended in mid-air like a bird in flight. Then I'd fall back down, sending my partner even higher. All was fine until one of us fell off. When we played with the skipping rope, it wasn't about how high we jumped, but how low—a tiny, perfectly timed hop, just enough for the rope to slide under our feet as we swung it faster and faster, till the rope whirled in a blur. Whoever jumped one hundred times in one go was the winner. Then we made it progressively harder, jumping cross-armed, jumping one-legged, and then jumping once for two passes of the rope. That was the hardest. No one could do the double-pass more than thirty times without snagging the rope.

When there were no other kids to play with, In-sook and I played our stones games. After In-sook had first shown me the stones game, I'd been winning more and more. In-sook hated losing, so she cheated and clumsily, too. I hated cheats. Where was the fun if everyone cheated?

One time, after losing one too many games and my penalising her for breaking the rules, In-sook threw her stones at my face, smacking my forehead and cheek.

"It's a dumb game! I'm not playing it anymore," she said, her voice faltering with fear as I touched a spot of blood on my forehead.

"You still lose, you cheat," I shot back.

Then from out of nowhere she said, "Well, you don't even have a name."

"I do, too."

"Ah-gha isn't a name, you stupid. Everybody knows that. My mom said you haven't got a real name." She stuck her tongue out, and walking away, chanted, "Ah-gha, ugg-gha, uk-kha-kha, Ah-gha, ugg-gha, uk-kha-kha . . ."

I flew after her, jumped on her back and pelted her with my fists. She squealed, running in circles to get me off. She succeeded, but not before I'd yanked out some of her hair.

We both got a good whipping from Aunt later. In-sook never seemed to mind getting spanked. She cried a lot, screaming and carrying on during it, then as soon as it was over, she quickly forgot, laughing and running around. I didn't. I was quiet during the whipping. I didn't feel I had the freedom to object. But I hated it and never forgot it.

In-sook's remark tugged at me all day. I also felt something was wrong with my name. All babies were called Ah-gha; it simply meant "baby." Until now, no one had made fun of my name. Ah-gha was my name; what other name could people call me by? Still, I couldn't toss away the nagging thought. I decided to ask Mom when next she came to visit.

Chapter Four

My days at Aunt's rolled into weeks, months, and then a whole year, my longest stay anywhere. With the repetition of days came constancy, then a sense of belonging and Saturday became the most important day of the week. The other days I thought of as waiting for Saturday to come around days. For Mom came to see me on Saturdays. Her visits validated me and sewed me, stitch by stitch, into the hem of her dress, reassuring me that I belonged to her.

Although she didn't come until lunch time, I kept watch in our backstreet from breakfast on. It helped me to ward off the fear that she might not visit, which happened from time to time. Waiting and concentrating on her was the offering of my devotion, like Aunt's morning prayers to her God.

Taxis rarely came through our dingy, narrow backstreet, so when Mom arrived in one, the neighbours, young and old, took notice. My friends swarmed around her like minnows in a pond, their mouths agape, eyes wide in honest admiration. She was unlike anyone we normally saw, with her thick hair cropped neatly below the ears in the latest fashion, a thin leather belt hugging her small waist in a pleated skirt, her silk stockings shimmering on her long legs down to her pumps. Then there was her smile, brighter than the sunniest day, as warm as Lee's bare bosom in deep winter. Mom was my surprise gift every Saturday but I never took it for granted as sometimes she didn't show up.

While I waited for her arrival, I played the familiar scenes over and over in my mind: Mom getting out of the taxi, her eyes searching, zooming in on me, me running to her, claiming her, burrowing in, losing myself in her plushness, as her clean, fresh scent cut through our backstreet's stench of urine-soaked alley gutters, fermented soybeans and kimchee. Then holding hands, we'd walk down our little pathway to the house as I glanced back to see if the neighbourhood moms were still watching; they were, standing in front of their homes, arms folded tight, long aprons hiding their unshaven legs, their mouths downturned, eyes narrow and unblinking in distrust and envy, gawking at my fashionable, modern Mom. (Most moms stayed home, following the old Korean precept of the ideal woman, "Hyun-Mo-Yang-Chuo," meaning, "Wise Mother, Obedient Wife." My Mom was not one of these.) Once inside, I'd open my arms wide, so she could take off my dirty clothes and carry me to the water pump, scrubbing out the caked-in grime on my neck, arms, and feet, then wash me thoroughly once more from head to toe, all the while scolding me. "Stomping around like a boy, filthy from head to toe. Look at your nails, all black! Are you really my girl?" But I'd grin ear to ear as I gave into her washing and scrubbing. I never minded her scolding, it came at me like a tender lullaby. I was so happy that I could float away like a soap bubble.

But it wasn't only me who waited for Saturday. Others did, too, because Mom came bearing gifts, sometimes big, other times small: a fancy jar of face cream for Aunt. For all of her Spartan ways, Aunt loved makeup and beautiful clothes; her mantra was, "Good grooming gives you wings." A handsome notebook and eraser-tipped pencils for Kang-jin, erasers that actually erased instead of streaking up the paper. A fine lace-collared blouse for Mi-hae. In-sook and I each got a tin of hard candies, the kind that our friends never saw or tasted. Mom brought these from the PX on the US army base in a small city called Uijongbu, north of Seoul. Mom was a secretary for a colonel, and as an army employee she lived in the camp with other workers. Years later, Uijongbu would become famous as the setting for the American television series, M*A*S*H. Her journey to visit me took her over two hours each way.

Saturday also meant a feast, for she brought food too, a rotisserie chicken, a thick joint of roast beef and sweets. Beef was a rare luxury. We normally sliced our meat thinly, cooking it with vegetables or putting it in soups. Even when barbecuing, we cut it paper-thin, wrapping it with a piece of lettuce, adding scallions, pickled radish and carrots. And she brought an American cake—a lemon-flavoured, cream cake that turned into a heavenly mush as we ate it.

On one such Saturday visit, even Kang-jin showed a soft side: he reached over the dinner table and tousled my hair. I flinched, pulling away instinctively, so unexpected was his action. He said to Mom, "I'm so glad Ah-gha lives with us. I now have two baby sisters!" Then uncharacteristically shy and half stammering, he added, "Aunt . . . you are looking younger . . . prettier each time you visit. People could mistake you for a high school girl, like Mi-hae. I bet you looked just like Ah-gha when you were little. She's going to grow up just like you . . . a beauty!"

"What about your own mother, you ungrateful rascal! Have you got nothing good to say to me?" Aunt said.

"Yes, he's all grown up, flirting already. Soon I'll be seeing my grand nephews," said Mom, who was twenty-eight, just nine years older than him. "I'm counting on you to help and protect Ah-gha," said Mom, putting a large piece of pork on his rice bowl, as people did to show affection. Kang-jin blushed, bowing and nodding, and promised her, "I will, Aunt. I sure will," he then put some pork on Mom's rice bowl.

"I am the one who raised him and there he goes worshipping you," Aunt said, in a mock sneer.

I kept my face down, but In-sook kicked me under the table, biting back her giggles, goading me to laugh. We'd never seen Kang-jin like this, coy, tying himself in knots, trying to cosy up to my Mom. Also, he was lying, all a flaming red lie. He was never a cuddly, older brother, not even to In-sook. But I'd never say anything bad about him to Mom. Living at Aunt's, I learned the hard way never to be a tattletale.

Early on, I was drawn to Kang-jin. Who could resist when he looked like an action hero in a comic book come to life: the wide-set eyes under thick brows; a broad intelligent forehead, if a forehead could be intelligent; a much-prized straight nose; and a manly square jaw. To top it off, he was a brilliant student. But my attraction faded quickly: no one wanted to have a book thrown at them or be kicked in the butt. Kang-jin was prone to do this to us, casually and often. He lumped the two of us, me and In-sook, as noisy, dirty little pests, just plain unfit-to-be-in-the-same-room runts. He had a quick and mean temper with us but he was courteous to our neighbours, and patient and kind to their kids. Everyone envied Aunt. Kang-jin was destined for greatness, they gushed. We believed that too.

Under Aunt's instruction, Lee cooked and timed our family meals according to Kang-jin's study schedule and taste, his soup brimming with extra meat, his rice scooped up from the middle of the pot where it was most tender, moist yet fluffy. The pot never cooked rice evenly, leaving the top layer half raw and the bottom layer slightly burnt. In-sook and I didn't care for the middle part so we fought for the crunchy and nutty burnt layer at the bottom.

Mi-hae, the second born, a daughter, didn't complain about the reverence everyone showered on Kang-jin. He was the first and only son who carried the family's future on his shoulders. Only one thing irked her: having to wash her own clothes. Lacking time, Lee only washed and ironed Kang-jin's clothes. Mi-hae's vanity wanted her school uniforms blindingly white, that meant she had to wash and iron them daily herself—the white collar and handkerchief for her winter uniform, the white blouse and socks for spring and autumn. Mi-hae argued that if her delicate hands became large and coarse like Lee's, how could she ever hope to marry into a great family. Wasn't that Aunt's goal as well? But Aunt was unshakable. Kang-jin never touched water except to wash himself. He never set foot in the kitchen.

The business of Mi-hae's laundry led to our major falling out, where she taught me how things really stood.

Mi-hae's beauty stopped time. It was as if the eighth-century Chinese beauty, Yang Gui-bi herself was reincarnated in Mi-hae's body; the legend of Yang

Gui-bi's stunning beauty spread all the way to Korea
and Japan. Not only was she beautiful, it was said that
her skin shimmered like pearls. Unlike In-sook who
had dark skin, thought to be peasant-like, Mi-hae's
was porcelain white, her long neck smooth like polished marble that you wanted to glide your hand over.
Her abundant shiny hair tumbled down to her waist,
blacker than black, almost blue. Her face radiated sen-
suality and purity, beguilement and innocence. An
aura of blue-moon surrounded her; the faint, fine blue
veins under her skin meandering from her cheeks to
her gracefully sloping shoulders, down to her tapered
arms. Even the whites around her pupils had a blue
tint to them. In a certain light she looked almost trans-
lucent. Every night, she sat in front of the tall chest
mirror, combing her hair one hundred strokes with
camellia oil that made it gleam like mulberry silk, and
she watched herself in the mirror, hypnotised by the
impossible beauty staring back at her. Aunt warned
her about turning into a nine-tailed fox. The legend
has it that each night the fox transformed herself into
a beautiful woman, seducing men, eating their hearts
to keep herself human and forever young.

To my six-year-old eyes, Mi-hae seemed a fairy
princess, and I became her devoted acolyte. Each morning, I brought her a bowl of cold water, the beads of
condensation running down the bowl, fresh from the
water pump, never from the kitchen urn where the
water could have been sitting for days. I'd watch her

drink, dazzled by the way the water slid down inside her long, graceful throat, and the way she delicately sprinkled her face with the remaining water—the secret to her perfect skin and humming digestive system, she said. And in late summer, she let me help stain her toenails; she preferred me, she confided, as In-sook was clumsy and untidy. Students weren't allowed to colour their nails, but toes were hidden inside their white socks, so teachers couldn't see them. Aunt often said, "A Korean woman would drink cyanide, if it made her more beautiful." Staining toenails was far from being deadly, you just needed nimble fingers and a little patience.

For the perfectly stained nails: first, we picked the reddest touch-me-nots and also some of their green leaves. They grew everywhere, at the base of walls, along the little alleyways. Next, we crushed the blossoms in a bowl to a pulpy mush, then placed a small batch on top of each toenail, wrapping each one tightly with a touch-me-not leaf and tying it securely with a thread. Now the patience part: the toes must be kept wrapped, even while sleeping, no matter how itchy or throbbing they got from the tight binding, to let the flower dye work its way into the nails, staining them indelibly until the nails grew out. The longer you kept it on, the deeper the colour became. The result was lovelier and more subtle than the harsh-looking, easily chipped, painted-on nail varnish.

One winter afternoon, Mi-hae came home sweaty

and limping. Her bus had broken down midway, so she'd had to walk. She couldn't get another bus, as each one was so packed that the driver refused to open the door. I helped to get her socks off. The long walk and tight shoes gave her oozing blisters on the top of her toes and on her heel, the swollen skin falling away. I nursed her feet, putting on mercurochrome, and blowing on them to lessen the sting. She asked if I'd wash her socks. I was glad to do it; I'd seen her doing it many times. The next day, she asked me again sweetly, and this time, would I mind also washing the detachable white collar of her uniform. I didn't mind. And the next day, the same thing. As the days went by, out went the nice lilt in her voice, now sounding more like Aunt's telling Lee what to do. After several days of giving my services, I quit, disappearing before she came home. I went to Aunt's shop. At home, Aunt's running frantically was the norm, yelling at us, her hot hand ready to spank, but in the shop, I saw a different Aunt—a cool, brave businesswoman in the male dominated Korean society. I liked being in her shop. When she wasn't too harried, she taught me to sew various stitches on a patch of discarded fabric: a single file stitching, often used for temporarily holding two layers of fabric together; a loop stitching for button holes; a braid stitching for reinforcing and decorating; and ways to tie the ends, so the thread wouldn't unravel. She let me make cushions the size of my palm for her pins and needles. But more often than not, I simply watched her work as she glided the fabrics under the needle of her sewing machine to puncture and thread a straight line without stopping—tock, tock, tock, tock, tock—her foot pedals going up and down, up and down, in hypnotic rhythm. I could feel Aunt's calm focus. The sewing machine loved her: it hummed for her, it danced for her.

On that following Saturday, hoping to make Mom laugh, I imitated the way Mi-hae commanded me to do her laundry; her nose up, head tilted just so, eyes cool and innocent. I had a repertoire of people I mimicked for Mom's laughter—the way Aunt walked, like a soldier, with head, torso, and arms frozen together, but upon seeing a mirror, becoming a girl, pouting her lips, popping her eyes large, posing this way and that. I impersonated how In-sook attacked her rice-bowl at meals, plunging into it head first, her forelocks spilling over, eating rice, hair and all, like some furry animal digging in the earth. My best, however, was mimicking pop singers, which never failed to send Mom into a laughing fit and a bit of awe, too. Not only could I sing their songs exactly, I also could do the singers' unique ticks and inflections.

But this time, my mimicking Mi-hae backfired. Mom asked questions. She didn't like the way Mi-hae treated me. She spoke to Aunt, which turned into an argument. I'd not heard them arguing before. That evening after Mom left, Aunt called me and Mi-hae into the big room.

"Ah-gha-ya, come, sit next to me. And Mi-hae, you stand up and face Ah-gha. Lift your skirt," said Aunt. Mi-hae lifted up her skirt. "Above your knees!" Aunt ordered. Then taking the long whip that we all knew so well and feared, she brought down seven lashes on Mi-hae's calves, emphasizing each lash with, "Who . . . said . . . you . . . could . . . order . . . Ah-gha . . . around!"

I squirmed at each blow. The stick swished and struck Mi-hae's calves like iron sticking to a magnet, the swishing sound more terrifying than the actual whipping, but I didn't dare cup my ears. Mi-hae bit her lips, refusing to cry, but her body twitched with each blow. Aunt made her promise never to use me again, as the final lash came down on her calves. I felt horrible for her, but even worse for me, I was next.

Aunt then turned to me. "Ah-gha, you're old enough to know what to say and what not to say to your mom. Why do you worry her with the small things that go on between sisters? You are family. You come to me if you're unhappy, or if someone mistreats you. Understood?" I nodded, yes. "You both can go now."

It was over. I couldn't believe my luck.

Mi-hae, defiant, marched out, the mean red welts rising up like bloated worms on her white flesh.

The next day was Sunday. After breakfast, Mi-hae asked if I might come out to the yard, she wanted to talk. I was relieved she wasn't angry. She hobbled out, I followed. When we reached the far wall, she swung around and pinched my cheeks hard, her sharp nails digging in as she twisted my face upward, forcing me to stand on tiptoe. I cried out.

"Shut up, you filthy little tramp. You're a beggar, a bastard, a tattletale traitor. Why don't you just go back to where you came from?" she hissed, "I'll show you where you really belong!" She dragged me by my cheek and opened the outhouse door at the end of the wall. "Smell that? See that? That's where you belong, that's who you are. Don't you dare move and go crying to anyone, I swear I'll bring you right back and drop you into that hole and let you die, drowning in shit." She shoved me in, slamming the door.

I fell chest forward, the breath knocked out of me and hit the edge of the rectangular hole in the cement floor with my forehead. My head and right arm slid into the hole, dangling above a pool of faeces and muck, five feet deep. It was pitch black. The powerful stink choked me. Grabbing on to the edge of the hole, I lifted up my torso, and splayed my limbs across the hole. The narrow cement ground around the hole was slippery with melting urine and frozen bits of stray faeces softening under the heat of my hands and legs. One wrong move, I would slip and fall back into the hole. But I had more urgent fear: rats. They ruled the outhouse, swimming and skidding around the mounds of wet faeces in the hole and the ground above. Finally perched on all fours, I carefully circled around the hole, lining myself with the door. I pushed it with my back. The door didn't budge. Balanced on my knees,

I felt for the small door knob and tried turning it. It wouldn't turn, my hand was too slimy. Holding the knob, I gave my best bang on the door with the other hand. Just then the door flung open and I fell into a pair of thick legs.

"Tsk, tsk, tsk," Lee clicked her tongue. She lifted me up by the back of my shirt, holding me out like a dirty dishrag, saying, "You stink something awful."

Only then I heard the loud thumping in my heart. I cried, but the fear had drained the tears. Lee put me by the water pump, brought hot water from the kitchen and washed me. She didn't ask me what had happened and I didn't volunteer. I wanted to know what a "bastard" was but somehow felt ashamed to ask her. I'd ask Mom, I decided.

But Mom didn't show up on Saturday, nor the following one. Her missing one Saturday was not unusual, but two in a row, that had never happened. I was distraught and nervous, afraid of Mi-hae. I couldn't tell anyone and telling Aunt would only make things worse.

From the bottom left drawer of the tall chest, my old hiding place, I took out the candy tin. Everything of value I owned was inside: six American hard candies, five fine marbles, eight ten-won coins, and three five-won coins. With the tin in hand, I walked out of the house through the back alleyway. When I reached the church playground, I veered off left, onto the main thoroughfare, Mapo Boulevard. Turning left again I went up the long hill. Si-jang and home fell farther and farther away. This road was not as familiar to me as it was a hectic road, nothing good to explore for us kids, and unsafe too, with speeding cars, buses and trucks. But on this late Sunday morning, the street was empty of people, and fewer cars too. I'd been in buses with Mom when I first came to live with Aunt, so I knew what to do. I had a plan: I'd get on a bus and go to Uijongbu where the US army base was, and there, everyone would know where Mom was and I'd be taken to her. I'd tell her I'd come to live with her; I'd cook rice, clean and wash while she worked.

But soon I came to a hurdle: I couldn't get the buses to stop. They just sped away, right by me. One bus stopped at a stoplight, I went up to it, but it didn't open its door. Cars around me honked, all angry. I went back to the sidewalk and walked on. The street was empty, except for a lone teenager about Mi-hae's age coming out from a side street. Upon seeing me, she slowed as if she knew me, then came to a stop. I stopped too, but on guard. What if she was a friend of Mi-hae; she could tell on me. But she smiled kindly, even asked me where was I going, or was I lost. I said I wanted to get a bus to Uijongbu. "I am going that way myself. We can go together," she said, pointing to the hill. Grateful, I thanked her. We walked on side by side. She asked what I had in my hand. I didn't notice it till then that I was jingling with each step. "My candy tin," I answered.

"How pretty, where did you get it?"

"My Mom."

"What's in it?"

"Just things."

"What things, can I see?"

Now I was stumped, she'd been so kind, but I didn't want her touching it. I compromised. I held out the tin, and turned it around and around, so she could see the colourful drawings of candies in pink, green, red, and yellow, and the impressive black scribbles that went all around it. My coins, marbles, and candies rolled around inside.

"Wow, can I hold it?" she asked.

I hesitated.

"I'm not going to steal it," she said. "Here, why don't you hold my bag while I look at yours," she held out her paper bag. That seemed fair. I handed her my tin and took her bag which was surprisingly light. Then in a flash, she bolted, running into the side street with my tin. I simply stood there, watching her disappear. I opened her bag; there was nothing in it but some crumpled newspaper. I ran after her to the same side street, but she was gone. I plopped down on a low wall. The shock of it all sent hot spikes all over my skin. How could I have been so dumb? The money for the bus, candies I was going to eat on the bus, my best marbles, all gone. I sat and sat, furious, having no one to blame but my gullible, stupid self. Do I go back home then? No, I thought. I'm going to Mom no matter what.

I got up and continued on uphill. Eventually the road flattened, and just like the teenager said, I saw the bus-stop, with a few adults and a girl about my age with her mom waiting around. I mingled in. A bus arrived and people climbed aboard, the mom and the girl, too. An old woman stepped up next, I held onto her blooming skirt and followed up behind her. The driver didn't even look at me. I followed the woman to the back of the bus and sat in the last row, she by the window, me on the aisle. I had pulled it off! I was on my way, Mom would be proud. Then it dawned on me that I didn't know how long two hours actually was. But I caught on quickly. I heard the driver calling out the name of the place at each stop. All I had to do was to wait for Uijongbu. After a while, the old woman left so I moved into her window seat which gave me an unobstructed view outside: buildings, trees, buses, cars, people, undulating electrical wires like the edges of Mom's skirt, then the whole set repeating again and again. Excitement turned to boredom, then to anxiety. How much longer before the driver called out Uijongbu? People thinned out in the back of the bus. When my worry turned into panic, I went up to the driver and asked as politely as I knew how: "When will you call the stop for Uijongbu?"

"That's outside of Seoul, not my route," he said. That made no sense to me. Didn't all buses stop at all bus stops?

"But I'm going to Uijongbu, please take me there, you *have* to take me there," I insisted.

"Get back to your seat before you fall," he yelled.

At the next stop, he huffed himself up and surveyed the bus. "Who's responsible for this kid?" People shrugged, shaking their heads. "Where's your mom? How did you get in my bus? You need to leave." He was upset. He grabbed my wrist as if to pull me off the bus. I held tight onto the metal bar.

"No, I'm going to Uijongbu," I screeched, then I began wailing in fear.

People wanted to get off the bus, telling the driver to please open the door.

"No! I'm not opening the door till one of you take this girl," he shouted. It was not their responsibility, just open the door now the passengers argued. Still the driver refused. The passengers got up from their seats and began shouting obscenities at him.

"Open the door! You can't do this to us," one man yelled. Another rushed to the front, pushed the driver and got the door open. The driver fell, rolling down the steps, and hit the asphalt. People rushed out of the bus, but some gathered around the driver. He just lay there as if he was sleeping, but his legs were twisted into an unnatural position with his left foot bent backwards. The crowd grew bigger. A police car's harsh siren sounded as it approached. Two policemen got out, and parting the crowd, shook the driver gently. The driver came to, but when they tried to help him to his feet, he couldn't stand. How could he when his legs were all tangled up? An ambulance came and took him away. Then I was the only one still sitting inside the bus.

It was very late when the police finally brought me back home. It took a long time because they didn't believe my name really was Ah-gha. And I didn't know our address, only that we lived in Ah-hyun Dong, in Mapo District, near Si-jang and the large new church and that Aunt had a tailor's shop.

The anticipated whipping didn't come that night. Instead, Aunt herself brought me dinner, watched me while I ate, even putting a piece of soy-steamed mackerel on my rice. Even more unexpected: she let me sleep beside her that night, tucking me in, stroking my hair.

Chapter Five

A ray of golden autumn sunshine bathed the main room, turning the ageing yellow soybean-waxed floor into lush ochre. The light also fell on Uncle, on his broad forehead, noble nose, white ramie shirt and his open book. Uncle's preferred position was horizontal, laying on his side, his shoulder propped up with a cushion, his right hand under his chin and his left holding a fan. Soft music droned on from the radio by his pillow. Nothing moved, even his bamboo fan was closed and held close to his heart. It was as if time had fallen asleep. All was quiet too, although there was the background noise from the street, and the periodic, rhythmic muffled sound of Aunt's sewing machine next door. I knew that sound pattern well. When she ran it non-stop for a spell, it meant she was sewing the length of a dress. If she did a stop-and-go, she was working on a narrow corner, perhaps a shoulder, a collar or a 90 degrees turn of the hem.

I stood over Uncle, waiting for the sign. Without looking up, he spread out his left arm making a space. I slid in and nestled between him and the book. I looked at the pattern of images on the pages of his book. I didn't know how to read yet, let alone the squiggly Chinese characters on pages dotted with brown spots and the edges frayed with age. But I could read my Uncle well; no words were necessary between us.

When he lifted his fan I sat up, alert, then ceremoniously and carefully, I turned the fragile pages of his book from left to right, and settled back against his soft belly that rose and fell gently in tune with his breathing.

The sunlight wrapped around us like a blanket. Soon, Uncle's fan fell out from his limp fingers, his head fell forward as he fell asleep. He snored mildly, musically, like humming a song. Aunt's machine stopped and I dozed off.

"I'm back! Lee! I'm hungry!" In-sook stomped in, yelling, throwing down her schoolbag. She ran towards us and circled behind Uncle, clasping her arms around his neck, almost choking him, wanting to know what we were doing.

In-sook's arrival signalled the end of our peaceful afternoon.

Mild-mannered and soft-spoken, everything about Uncle was slow: he ate slowly, read slowly, spoke slowly, even seemed to listen to his radio slowly, with his eyes half-closed. He walked slowly too, like a stately ancient Korean aristocrat. His hands cupped behind his back, he led with his chin and stomach, his steps spread wide and purposeful, needing a bit more space around him than others. I was sure he never ran in his life, even when he was a kid like me.

Uncle belonged to me. That was one thing I felt deeply and that I alone was on his side. All his children were Aunt's pups, attuned to her moods, reading her silence, following her every word, even when she strung out curse words like lights on a Christmas tree. Uncle was treated like an itinerant lodger. Kang-jin and Mi-hae showed him little affection and never bothered to listen when he talked about his life as a doctor up north near the DMZ, the Korean Siberia as far as they were concerned. But Uncle's presence at home, no matter how infrequent, was an important facade for normalcy. It kept our neighbours' wagging tongues in their mouths. Aunt often nagged him to move his practise near home. But he always gave the same answer. In all his gentleness and slow talk, he'd say, how could he abandon his patients, and what about his relatives who needed his guidance as the elder of his clan?

In-sook claimed him, freely demanding his affection, anytime, anywhere, jumping on his lap, snuggling against him, pulling on his ear. I never claimed him but believed I earned our closeness. We were not blood-related; his love was not a given. Still, I felt he loved me as much as In-sook, if not more. After all, he trusted me enough to let me help when he prepared his medicines. What better proof could one ask for?

As easy going as he was, when it came to his medicines, he was meticulous. It involved elaborate steps. First, he brought out from our wall chest his medicine box. It was about as tall as I was. This box was made up of many small vertical and horizontal rows of drawers, each drawer containing various medicinal herbs—mulberries, mugwort, ginseng, gingko, and cinnamon, as well as exotic animal parts like horns from rhinoceros and bones from tigers, musk deer, sea horses, even scorpion, all dried and thinly sliced or finely ground up.

On a clean board, he spread out ten or twelve square pieces of white paper, in two rows, each paper slightly bigger than my hand. Onto these papers, he added precise amounts of herbs, weighing them carefully on his fine, miniature scale. He added up to ten different ingredients per piece of paper, a pinch of this, a sprig of that. Now the fun part: he folded each paper into a rectangular shaped packet, and like origami, it held together perfectly without glue. It was at this point, I assisted him. I put the packets into a white envelope on which Uncle wrote elegant Chinese characters. That was a batch. Then we repeated the steps all over again. When he had a stack of white envelopes, I put them into his leather medicine bag. I called it the treasure box. In the bag were tincture bottles, a box of herbs for making moxa sticks, round glass bowls for cupping treatment, a box of matches, a bottle of alcohol, cotton balls in a glass jar for sanitising the acupuncture needles, and finally, the heavy metal box where shiny acupuncture needles of various sizes were kept in a bed of cotton.

We never questioned his prowess as a traditional Korean doctor, although he never had to prove it. No one in the house ever got sick, except me: I occasionally got stomach aches. Then I became his willing patient. I couldn't recall if he ever healed me, but the bitter taste of his medicine was unforgettable. You had to pinch your nose to empty the packet into your mouth, where a portion of fine powder almost choked you, then you quickly washed it down with water, the foulness and bitterness lingering on long after. Mom's hard candies really helped, if there were any.

I preferred his acupuncture treatment to his herbs. Somehow I was more curious than afraid of it. He distracted you by tapping lightly around your stomach with his fingertips, then before you knew it, long and impossibly thin needles fluttered up and down on your stomach in tune with your breathing. You never felt them going in or coming out. Other times, he used his hand-made moxa sticks. He took a small amount of green-grey dried herb and turned it into a pyramid shape, the size of the tip of his little finger. He placed it just above and below my bellybutton and lit the tips. The moxa burned slowly in a bright orange colour, the delicate smoke wobbling upwards, the calming smell filling the room, and me feeling a warm glow spreading inside. The residual ash remained until Uncle pinched out the last of the burning moxa just before it got to my skin.

During this time, I envied In-sook terribly. Now that she was a first grader, she had no time for me. She found new friends of her own age in her class. She was learning things I didn't know. She carried around that alluring school bag on her back where she kept things, school books, lined notebooks, a pouch for her pencils and erasers, away from my prying eyes. At dinner table, she prattled on and on about her school, teachers and classmates. So when the occasion came that Aunt and Uncle, and Mom talked about my schooling, I listened with great interest.

Unfortunately it wasn't all to the good. I was lacking some very important information needed to enrol. It was quite possible I might miss starting school in the coming January, the beginning of the school year. I also understood why Mi-hae treated me badly, Mom's awkward position, and most sadly, why Uncle and I had to part our ways.

When Uncle came home, Kang-jin, Mi-hae and Lee slept in Kang-jin's small study room. The rest of us, Aunt, Uncle, In-sook and I, in the main room. In-sook was a quick and deep sleeper. I never fell asleep easily, drifting in and out, half-listening to Aunt and Uncle's soft chatter in Japanese which they often did whenever they wanted to keep things secret from us kids.

Their Japanese whispers were pleasing and relaxing, reassurance that all was well between them, and that meant with us too. I especially liked the way Aunt elongated and lingered on the ends of her sentences, unexpectedly feminine, for her.

But suddenly, their mild chatter turned harsh, soon switching to Korean, words spitting out, tempers rising.

"I will *not* dishonour my ancestors by putting a bastard on my family registry," shouted Uncle.

I never imagined Uncle capable of shouting or showing anger. I was fully awake now.

"Shhh, you'll wake up the girl," Aunt half-whispered. "Please listen. It's hard enough to come up with kids' high school tuition, but university! Kang-jing's is just around the corner, then Mi-hae the year after. We can't afford them. But Ah-gha's mom promised to pay for both. What else can we do?"

"I'll take care of my kids' education!"

"You? Really! You must be joking. When was the last time you brought home money? Always empty-handed, and we all know why, don't we? All because of that bitch up north. Don't deny it, don't even try. And here I am, slaving away to make ends meet. How desperate does a person have to be to use her own baby sister! I'm at my wits end. My shop won't last much longer. Do you see any other stores like mine on my street? All chased out. Gone! People don't custom-make their clothes anymore. Why would they? See those big new shops popping up everywhere? That's where they go now. They can pick whatever they want off the rack and walk out. How can I compete with that? You tell me."

Uncle remained silent.

"And I thought you liked Ah-gha. You certainly spend a lot of time with her. And she follows you around like a puppy. Come on. Don't you feel sorry for her? She is seven and still without a name. Put her in your family registry. It's a small favour. She can't go to school without a birth certificate."

Uncle finally spoke, his voice low and steely, "Did you ever ask me if she could live with us? She's a stain, a disgrace. I put up with her, sure, she's a good kid, but a bastard. A bastard! And not even my *own* bastard. No better than a stray dog!"

"It's 1966, not 1866. No one cares anymore. Who do you think has been paying our rent all this time? Not you. Not me. Her mom!"

Uncle cut in. "Nothing good can come from this. It's bad luck! And your sister, she's damaged goods, too, a whore for all I know, parading around in her fancy American clothes. I knew she was bad news the minute I saw her, those squinty eyes, that big mouth, ready to gobble men up. Even our innocent Kang-jin's all over her. And just because she brings us Yankee leftovers, I should feel grateful, bow down and dirty my family name? No. It's her bastard, let her figure it out. I won't shame my ancestors. Imagine the curse they'll put on me. It'll destroy us all. Then it'll be on your head! And one more thing: you lied to me. 'Only for a couple of weeks,' you said. She's been here over two years, *dammit!* I won't put up with it anymore. You get her out. Sooner the better!"

Disgust shook his voice. He kicked off his blanket and stormed out, slamming the shoji door for good measure.

My face burned as if I had stuck my head in an oven, my toes curled inwards, my eyes unblinking. Then the scene of our after-dinner stroll last Saturday flooded over me. Everything made sense now.

Aunt cherished her after-dinner stroll ritual, perhaps the only time when she could relax, letting the wind cool her face, the walk settling her stomach. Always the decider, she led the walk, and we, usually In-sook, Lee and I, followed. But last Saturday, it was only Aunt, Mom, and me. We barely reached the hill of Mapo Boulevard, when Mom and Aunt began discussing my school enrolment, and that quickly spilled onto other matters, too, the kind kids shouldn't hear. But so whipped up in their own concerns, they didn't know I heard them, too.

"Unni, please talk to your husband. If we don't get Ah-gha's birth registry done this month, she won't go to school next year. Who else can I turn to?" Mom said.

"I'll see what I can do, but you know him. You know how he gets when it comes to his family name. Honestly, I don't get it. What's so great about his rotten ancestors? They did nothing for me. No money ever fell from their sky on my lap," said Aunt.

"I've got a good job now, and the colonel promised me that senior secretary position. Then I can take care of Kang-jin and Mi-hae's university tuition."

"Alright, I'll talk to him again, but you have to do your part. Promise you'll go out with Mr. Hong."

Looking frustrated, Mom said, "Unni, please. You know he's older than our dead father, he's already got two wives and all those grandkids. He gives me the creeps. He smells. I don't think he ever brushed his teeth in his entire life."

"All he wants is to make you happy. Don't you want to give Ah-gha a proper home? Go out with him. He's crazy about you, and like that song—he thinks the sun rises and sets with you. He'll even adopt Ah-gha to give her his last name. You think this kind of offer comes everyday? You think you're so special. You think you'll be pretty forever. No. It's the youth that's pretty, and you don't have much of that left. Wake up! How many times do I have to tell you? Nothing good will ever come from working for Americans. Who knows when they'll just pack up and leave? Where will you be then? What will you do? My advice? Stick with Koreans. Mr. Hong owns five buildings. Five! You are lucky he wants you. Just go out with him one night, that's all I ask."

Since that night of Uncle's outburst, I could no longer look him straight in the eye. He was the scariest of them all because he never let you know what he was really thinking, how he really felt. The fun and the tender moments we shared were all fake, confusing me thoroughly, turning my trust upside down. At least Kang-jin and Mi-hae hated me, right to my face. My *nunchi* wasn't so good, after all.

When Uncle came back home the next time, he was the same as before, the same soft smile, the same kindly, easy going manner. It was as if nothing had changed. But I avoided him. He didn't seek me out either.

In the end, I didn't get Uncle's last name. The father's name on my birth registry was left blank. I took on Mom's surname, Kim, the same as Aunt's. Women's surnames didn't change to their husbands' when they married. Only the children took on the father's surname as this practice helped to avoid marrying a relative. The last name also could distinguish a commoner from an aristocrat by the location of the ancestors, such as the town and the province. Despite the tidal wave of Western influence flooding in after the war, over a thousand years of Confucian teachings still ran deep. The blank spot left in my birth certificate meant I was a bastard. Each of my teachers would make a mental note that I was a child from a woman of loose morals, a woman with a dark past, and therefore, a bad seed.

About my Father: I never found the courage to ask. Whenever Mom visited, my underlying anxiety about her leaving again took over, making me forget things. And when I did remember, I never found the right moment: I didn't want to ruin our short time together with this uncomfortable subject that no one talked about. And Aunt wasn't someone I could freely ask about things that concerned me. So I floated between two worlds, Mom's and Aunt's, doing my best not to cause ripples.

The following January, I started my first grade. My name tag read Su-young Kim, legally, my new name.

Chapter Six

The sun sat low over the roofs on a peaceful Saturday afternoon. I was thoroughly content because Mom had arrived on a visit. In the kitchen, Lee was preparing dinner, grilling corvina fish Mom had brought, the delicious smell wafting out to the yard and into our room. In-sook and I were lying on our bellies, drawing dolls. We did our homework lying down, too. The low table came out only for meals. Mom was reading a magazine, sitting next to us.

Then Mom ruined this idyllic Saturday afternoon by asking me how my piano lessons were going. This was a very awkward question so I dived deeper into my doll drawing, as if I was struggling with a very difficult section.

Paper-doll making was huge with my classmates and with In-sook's too so I was hoping to divert Mom's attention from piano lessons to dolls.

In-sook made an exception to her rule of ignoring me and we made paper-dolls together, but there was a reason, Aunt's sharp scissors. The most important part of paper-doll making is having a pair of sharp scissors. Together we stole a pair from Aunt's shop. We were always careful to put them back exactly as we found them so we were never caught. If we had been caught, we decided that being punished together was best as Aunt would be exhausted faster.

We didn't simply draw a girl and cut her out. No, we created a whole world for her: a house with her own bedroom and many other rooms; a huge kitchen, its shelves full of food; a large yard with blossoming trees and a spanking new water pump; even a piano of her own. My doll slept on a flower-patterned pillow under the matching blanket. She had mom and dad, a great many clothes, summer and winter school uniforms, a Sunday dress, Korean traditional dress, hats, bags, scarves. The greater the detail, the more alive she and her world became.

Making the dresses was the most exciting and intricate part. It was the whole point of playing paper-dolls. The steps were: first fold a large piece of paper. Then from the folded edge, draw the collar and sleeves, and moving on down. Then with the paper still folded, cut out the dress, snipping around the neck hole for the doll's head to get in and out. When you open up the folded paper, the front and back of the dress will match, attached at the shoulders. Next, cut a short line on the back from the neckline, like for a zipper in the back of a real dress. For the final touch, draw the details on the backsides with equal care: a belt on her back if she had one on the front; if it were a polka dot dress, polka dots on the back too, including the buttons or a zipper. Never skimp the backside just because you don't see it right away. Lastly, carefully pull the dress over the doll's head, hanging it on her shoulders. Now she's ready for a fashion world.

Mom asked again about my piano lessons and I vaguely answered that I'd missed a few. Then *whack*, she smacked my head with her magazine. "Don't you know how important your piano lessons are? It's for your future!"

In-sook threw down her pencil and shot out of the room. She knew the drill: Aunt punished us both, equally, for not minding each other's bad acts. My head didn't really hurt, but I cried out. She'd never hit me and meant it before.

"Don't you ever skip them again. Do you understand?"

I refused to answer. I was angry. I was blameless.

"How long have you stopped going?"

I kept on drawing the doll, buying time to think. If I answered her, Aunt would punish me later for being a tattletale. It was Aunt who said I wasn't going any more. Who was I supposed to listen to? I lived with Aunt every day, Mom only on Saturdays.

Mom swept away my papers. "How long?"

"Two weeks," I admitted.

She walloped my bottom. This time, it really stung.

"Not my fault!" I yelled. "Aunt said we have no money!"

"Nonsense. Of course she does. I give it to her every month!" Now her face turned bright red. "You'll go back, starting Monday. I'll take care of your aunt." She got up and marched out to Aunt's shop. They fought. It was their first real fight.

Until two weeks ago, every day, Monday through Friday, I went to the home of Miss Chan, my piano teacher, for lessons. Mom said I sang before I could talk. One of her musician friends told her that I should take up the piano, the most complete instrument for learning music. So I began piano lessons just before I started my first grade. But going to Miss Chan's house wasn't just about learning to play the piano. It opened up a whole new world. It showed me how differently other people lived and behaved. And then there was the music, a world all its own.

Whenever I got near to Miss Chan's street, I slowed down. Our backstreet squeezed in as many homes as it could. Her street had only six houses, three on either side, and no buses, or trucks whizzing by although it was wide enough. My neighbourhood was unprotected; no gate, anyone could walk into anyone's yard. To keep the burglars away, we slept with a long stick behind the sliding door tracks. On Miss Chan's street, the houses not only had proper gates and front doors, some had trellises of clinging vines, dotted with colourful morning glories, their trumpet-like blossoms opening and shutting as they followed the sun through the day. Bulbous white hydrangea balls burst out from dense green leaves, making friendly borders between houses, while the dogwood trees stood aloof, here and there, melancholy, awash in their wispy white blossoms. I loved these dogwood trees, especially from afar; they gave the illusion of being flat, barely three dimensional, defused like someone's loose watercolour. In my neighbourhood, nothing grew except occasional wild daisies and touch-me-nots that stuck out from the dirt along someone's wall. Her street smelled of fresh open air; ours, a permanent fetid odour that briefly washed away when someone cooked afresh.

The first thing that greeted me at Miss Chan's house was the garden; the last of peonies, fading, drooping from the summer swelter; and ruby-red begonias and dahlias in purple, white and pink, that didn't mind the heat. In the back, their vegetable garden thrived with herbs, eggplants, tomatoes, and green peppers that hung like miniature lanterns. Sometimes, when I had to wait for my lesson in the waiting hall, the gentle and soft-stepped teacher's mother brought me a plate of tomatoes, sliced thinly, their juice spilling over, the clusters of seeds glistening like jewels. She sprinkled white sugar all over them, making tomatoes as sweet as a piece of fruit. I'd eat them slowly in small bites that Mom would be proud of. If I were at home, I'd have swallowed them whole, then licked the plate clean.

But the most incredible thing about Miss Chan's home was the outhouse. It was inside. At our home, every time I had to use the outhouse, I stopped to remind myself: hold steady, don't fall, make sure to take a deep breath, enough to last till you got out, and watch out; whatever you do, don't step on those squiggly maggots, whose popping sound under your shoes made you jump. When the pit got full, the mound of faeces came all the way up, nearly touching our bottoms; then, the outhouse cleanup man came with two buckets attached to a long yoke that he carried on his shoulders. He scooped up faeces and muck with a long ladle, filling the buckets to the brim, then he waddled back out, emptying them into his dump truck. He repeated this until the hole was empty. When he drove away, the muck spilled out, leaving a trail of stink that stayed for days. Once I saw a neighbourhood toddler plopped on a trail of wet faeces playing with a swarm of wriggling maggots. She picked them up one by one with her chubby little fingers, her face all scrunched up and ate them.

Even in public bath houses and at school we had to squat, but at Miss Chan's, all I had to do was walk, barefoot, down a clean wooden hallway that extended to the bathroom. Inside it, I sat on a spotless white ceramic bowl and afterwards, pulled on the chain handle by the wall, and like magic, water swooshed everything away, out of sight.

I told In-sook about it; she said I was lying. I told Aunt about it; she said I jabbered too much. When I told Lee, she was all agog, oohing and aahing, listening to me like it was some fantastic fairytale.

Another thing that made me stop on her street was music, sometimes her students would be playing, and occasionally Miss Chan herself. I'd never heard classical music before, only the Korean popular music from Uncle's radio, where the songs of regret, sadness, and longing warbled out. Even the happy tunes sounded only begrudgingly happy, more like a mad cry against the unjust world. But Miss Chan's playing was other worldly, uplifting, and orderly. The first time I heard her play, it stopped me dead in my tracks. Each of her notes pinged clear and singular, yet in harmony with others, so pleasing they were that I wanted to hold them in my palm, but they slid off like dew on drooping leaves. Another time, the notes hung in the air like rain drops that forgot to fall, vivid as if I could see them, I hung on, too. Then in slow motion, they all tumbled down into a rainbow of sound and rhythm. I became light and bubbly, something inside of me woke up, wanted out and to meld with this other thing. Everything else fell away; I'd stepped into a world made only of sound. I felt giddy like seeing Mom on a Saturday. I belong here, I said to myself, this is where I belong. And that was how music became my other Mom—a benevolent, joyful, embracing, yet always available Mom.

One Friday, I caught Mom standing outside, watching me play through the small window. She'd made a special trip to hear me play but didn't want to disrupt my lessons, she said. Miss Chan later told her that I should get a piano of my own. "She'll need to practice more. She's got talent. It's been only a year, and she's already playing sonatas. But here's what sets Su-young apart: she feels the music from inside out, and that's a rare thing."

Mom bowed to Miss Chan over and over, thanking her, squeezing her hands, promising that I would get a piano of my own. It was embarrassing and strange to see my elegant Mom acting like other moms at school, bent from the waist, desperately seeking teacher's favour for her kid.

Unfortunately, Aunt didn't think too highly of my piano lessons. "No more lessons," she had said a few weeks ago when I asked for my weekly lesson fee. "We don't have that kind of money. Enough is enough. Who does she think you are, giving you piano lessons, putting ideas into your head. Piano is for rich people. We've no use for it."

"But Mom said I'm to be a pianist."

"You do as I say! Your mom's got her head up her ass, is what it is. Always starting something she can't finish, doing things without thinking. And don't you talk back at me! Do that again and you'll get a whipping."

That was the end of my lessons. And now, good luck

to Mom, who went to fight to get my piano lessons back. She didn't have a chance. No one who went up against Aunt came out winning. I tried to concentrate on drawing a doll but couldn't, my ears stretched to the wall, listening.

"She's got a talent. Everyone says so," Mom said.

"Wake up! Get the cobwebs out of your brain. Piano lessons, what a joke! If my In-sook took piano lessons, that teacher would say the same thing to me. Can't you see? She's just buttering you up to make money from you. Don't chase after rich people's games, your legs aren't long enough for it. Tears are the only thing waiting for you and your daughter."

"Have I asked you to pay? I am paying."

"If you got that kind of money, get a house and take Su-young with you. I won't take your nonsense in my house. So blind. You never think things clearly. How could you let go of an opportunity like Mr. Hong? He could have bought Su-young a piano, easy."

"So that's what this is about. Getting back at me for not going out with that stinking, disgusting corpse. I am *not* doing that again, no matter who you try to stick me with next. No more! I'm done."

I kept drawing, trying to push out their ugly noise. I was used to Aunt's fights, her words deadly as viper's venom. But Mom, she didn't even shout convincingly, her voice cracking and sputtering. Still I admired her for it; Mom going against Aunt was like me going against Mi-hae. Just not done.

"Even if you've got ten tongues hanging out of your mouth, you've still got nothing to say! I raised you since you were born, and you've tossed me your kid too. Fine, I will raise her, but you do what I say."

"I've got a good job now. I'll take Ah-gha away sooner than you think."

"Do whatever you want. Just don't blame me later for your dumb decisions. Mark my words, Mr. Hong's the best thing that'll ever come your way."

My pencil had a mind of its own. The screechier they got, the scarier the doll got. Black circles around her eyes grew menacing, wide and hollowed out; her hair shot out, electrified.

Mom didn't win the fight. I never went back to Miss Chan. I never got a piano. We never talked about my piano lessons again. Around that time, I stopped badgering her about us living together, too.

But one good thing came out of my piano lessons; I'd already made a home in music. It followed me everywhere. Rather, I followed it, and soon, I found a way to be with music again—in American churches. Churches began sprouting in every corner of Seoul. In fact, my Aunt built a church of her own, from scratch.

Chapter Seven

Aunt's eyes were shut tight, her fists clenched to her heart. She was sitting on a small cushion, rocking her body back and forth as if in a trance, her lips mouthing furiously, "Oh, God, oh, Father, my saviour, forgive this sinner, save this wretched daughter, only through your grace and love, I shall walk through the gates to your kingdom." Next to Aunt, Uncle prayed, doubled over, his forehead on the floor, looking out of place—a Chinese medical doctor in a Korean *hanbok* that he insisted on wearing at all times. His huge, rounded sleeves and wide robe spread about him, making an island for himself. He would have looked more at home in a Buddhist temple. But here he was, prostrate, praying to a Christian God, although he didn't quite carry on like Aunt and other parishioners; it wasn't his way. Lee was also bent in prayer not far from them. Kang-jin and Mi-hae sat near Lee, their faces blank with boredom. Other worshippers swayed, their passions rising, whisper-shouting their pleas in fits and starts. Then Aunt called out, "Oh father, father, father." Following her lead, other parishioners joined in, raising their arms and waiving, in a hypnotic unison, chanting, "Oh father, father, father." We, a dozen or so kids, cramped against the wall, squirmed— some frightened, some embarrassed, some stifling giggle-fits. I was more practical. I worried that this rickety second floor room might collapse from the swelling, pulsating energy that rose and rose to a fantastical pitch, especially when Pastor Lim stepped into the pulpit and took over the prayers. The room was just enough for sixty or so people but there were well over a hundred. There was only one way in or out: a flight of stairs that bent and creaked with every step, just wide enough for one person.

Aunt prayed at least six times a day that I knew of: when she woke up at dawn, before going to bed, before each meal (when we all prayed together), and before she rolled up the steel door in front of her shop. She also went to the dawn prayer meetings on Tuesdays and Thursdays, and the Bible studies on Wednesday and Saturday evenings, where every study began and ended with prayers. And no need to mention the numerous prayers throughout Sunday at the church.

All our family members had to go to church. In-sook and I attended Sunday service, Sunday school and the church lunch. The Sunday church lunch was a weekly celebration, a generous banquet. Women parishioners took turns cooking during the service so it'd be ready right after. For us kids, and perhaps for adults too, this Sunday lunch was the best part of the church-going.

Before Aunt discovered Pastor Lim, she didn't hold any strong beliefs. She wasn't even superstitious like many Koreans. She never went to the popular palm or birthdate readings, nor to a shaman to pray for good fortune. Then one day, when Uncle went back up north, forgetting his radio, she took it to her shop, hoping it would also give her pleasure, or at least some distraction; she was weary of life, the exhaustion and fear of the future crushing her spirit. Then by chance, she heard Pastor Lim on the radio. He talked about how life didn't end with this one, but that an eternal joy waited in heaven; the more suffering in this life, the more glory waited in the next. Be poor, be humble, be simple, for it was easier for a camel to go through the eye of a needle than for a rich man to enter the kingdom of heaven. It wasn't her children that she must live for, but for her soul, for her God.

Hope and new purpose replaced her bitterness and sadness. It was as if she had been living in death, but now she knew she was simply waiting to shed her old skin. She would be reborn. She tuned in to Pastor Lim again the next day and the next. Her rage and regret fell away, she felt exhilaration she hadn't felt for years, she no longer mourned her glorious life in North Korea before her marriage—it was all vanity. So with her usual single-mindedness, Aunt hunted Pastor Lim down.

Pastor Lim was in his late sixties, revered in the Korean Baptist communities in Seoul and Tokyo, Japan. He had studied at Tokyo University, an unheard of accomplishment for a Korean, and for decades he travelled back and forth between Japan and Korea, working as a missionary and leading a congregation in the Korean ghetto in Tokyo. When Aunt finally got an interview with him, she pleaded with her fiery charm and passion: wasn't it time that he returned to Korea? What about the thousands of souls in his homeland who need to be saved, just as he had saved hers? Pastor Lim was moved. He couldn't remember the last time someone pursued him with such divine ecstasy, believing in him even more than he himself.

Aunt got him to promise to move to Seoul and lead her congregation. She also confessed that she didn't have a church yet, but would build one, just for him.

After the Korean war ended in 1953, humble little churches like Aunt's mushroomed everywhere with the help of American missionaries who had had a steady presence in pockets of Korea since 1884. In Korean, the word 'America,' rendered in Chinese characters, meant "Beautiful country." America stood for all things beneficent, progressive, and humane. Without its aid, South Korea's rapid economic growth wouldn't have been possible. North Korea was less lucky. With the Soviets occupying it, North Korea turned inward, going dark against the world. Still, Aunt's feelings towards America were complicated. On one hand, she was grateful. She said that her Christian God made all Koreans the same height, levelling the old class system of aristocrats and commoners, the powerful and the broken. But she also bristled at the physical presence of Americans. Invasion is invasion, she said, whether they invade with cruelty, like Japan, or bearing gifts, like Americans; either way, they were on your back, everything had a price.

Aunt's free spirit chose a Protestant church, preferring to talk to her God directly and not through lesser saints in Catholic churches. She built her one room church in a dilapidated building, taking to heart what Jesus said: "for where two or three are gathered together in my name, I am there among them." Then diligently converting worshippers door to door, street to street, she bought more spaces; a room next door, floor up, floor down. Soon the entire building became a Baptist church with a large cross nailed to the rooftop. Pastor Lim joined her, just as he promised. She appointed herself elder.

But Aunt being a Christian, a church elder, no less, didn't stop her from cursing. I thought only the uneducated cursed, but no, Aunt cursed often and with great imagination. Every time she cursed, I felt embarrassed for her, as if she had farted or exposed her breasts in public. And as her business slowed, her cursing rose to another level, more varied, more vivid, as persistent as the smell on a fishmonger's apron. The most colourful image to date was when she accused Uncle of having an affair with a woman up north: "You and that nasty bitch, I'll bet you pull her pubes out with your teeth!" That was memorable because I had a hard time picturing Uncle doing it. I didn't know what pubes were then, but it sounded painful and vile. But one thing Aunt didn't do, she didn't hold a grudge for long, most of her angers coming and going like thundershowers. We felt bad when she had to work through the night to meet a rush order. We felt even worse when she complained there wasn't enough work at her shop. She was the centre of our lives. Her fearlessness was our strength, her fears, ours. My Mom was a magnificent weekend guest.

Mom and Aunt were born in North Korea where they lived a very comfortable life. Aunt didn't want to get married but to work alongside Grandpa in his mining company that she hoped to inherit. But marriage inevitably came for her and the war brought the sisters to the South.

My great-grandparents on both sides boasted first born sons. Then to my grandparents' great disappointment, a daughter, my Aunt, came first. Grandma quelled her shame by taking it out on Aunt, punishing her in ways big and small. She just couldn't warm to her baby girl, wouldn't even try. She hated Aunt's drooling mess, her mindless gurgling. When her first words were "appa, appa" meaning "daddy, daddy," as she waddled over to Grandpa, it felt like a slap to Grandma. Aunt in turn, as babies instinctively sensed, preferred the nanny, screaming whenever Grandma tried to hold her. Grandma couldn't bear to change Aunt's nappies either, a reminder of her failure; instead of a little red pepper thing proudly poking out, she only saw a slit between Aunt's blubbery legs. The slit of shame, pain, blood. Grandma put boys' clothes on Aunt, even on her first day at school and beyond. Aunt told us that she had a flat chest because she never got her mom's milk, only the nanny's that she had to share with her twins.

But Grandpa doted on Aunt. When he lifted the bundled up newborn girl, he held a miracle. He poured all his love on her, even after Grandma gave him three sons. Only Aunt could sit on the right of Grandpa at mealtimes, free to go in and out of his study. Only she accompanied him on his morning walks. With no affection coming her way, Grandma sought comfort in her three sons; she adored them, wanted more. But another girl, my Mom, was born. A year later, Grandma died during childbirth, the baby boy died too. Aunt, already a formidable young woman, ran the household like a general, adding raising my Mom to her list of things to do. Mom grew up in worshipful fear of Aunt.

Despite or because of Grandpa's spoiling her and the frost between her and Grandma, Aunt grew up proud and aloof, earning the nickname, "the ice Empress." So cold she was, people whispered, that nothing grew in her shadow. But Aunt revelled in her nickname. It gives you a spine, she told us. She was a striking woman—serious, independent and sharp-eyed for business. Her brothers grumbled, bitter at Grandpa's preference for her; who ever heard of a woman running a company? This wasn't some clothing or food shop, but a mining company, full of men. But they came to accept her iron-willed dominance at home and in business. She became indispensible for Grandpa, often travelling with him, even accompanying him to Manchuria, where he had an ambition to expand his mining enterprises through his Japanese connections.

Spellbound by her cool, haughty beauty and wit, not to mention the wealth, many a strong, young northern man fell hard for her. Aunt took pleasure in their pursuit and eventual suffering. But no one moved her heart, until one cloudy spring day.

It was a day when cherry blossoms rained down on their lush Japanese garden. Aunt saw a tall young man standing with his back to her. Pale pink blossoms fell in pairs and triplets on this poised young man's thick black hair and the shoulders of his smartly cut Western coat. From her immaculate veranda, Aunt could see his slender, gentleman's hands, holding a black bowler hat behind him. She noticed the hands right away because no one around her had clean fingers, including Grandpa who liked to feel the dirt and ore with his hands. Aunt stood transfixed, as a strange sensation ran through her heart. Then as if he felt her presence, he turned his head, gazed at her with his soft, melancholy eyes, bowed slightly and turned back, once again meditating on the resplendent beauty of Grandpa's spring garden. That was all it took for Aunt to fall in love.

The tall young man with melancholy eyes was Uncle, coming up from the South to visit his friend, one of Aunt's brothers. Koreans had a saying: Southern Man, Northern Woman. Northern women were known for their beauty, southern men for their gentlemanliness.

That was the legend Aunt told us—how they fell in love the day when the cherry blossoms rained. But she didn't fall in love that day. That was the glossy version. The truth told a darker tale; Aunt saw this southerner as the means to escape death and find a haven below the 38th Parallel.

After repeated attempts for centuries, the Japanese finally succeeded in invading and occupying Korea. From 1910 to 1945, they ruled with an unimaginable savagery. One of the first things Japanese armies did, when they came into a village, was to poison the wells, killing anyone who drank the water. That was considered their gentle warning.

When the Japanese eventually moved up to the north of Korea, they began promoting industrial development in the rugged northern lands. Grandpa, who was struggling with a failing coal mining and steel mill business, saw an opportunity. He would collaborate with the Japanese, turning his back on his country. He bragged of working with the Japanese, but everyone knew he worked for the Japanese. They hated him for it, but some envied him, too.

Within a few years, Grandpa's business flourished, eventually expanding it all the way up north of the Dooman River that bordered China. Grandpa was one of the first to change his surname to Japanese, from Kim to Kimoto and mandated all his employees do the same. Only Japanese was spoken at home and in his office. Grandpa sent his second son to Japan, who would become a member of the Japanese Imperial Army. Grandpa also built an impressive Japanese home that included a Japanese rock garden, and an elaborate Shinto shrine, although he didn't practice it. He effectively became Japanese.

Grandpa thrived in both societies, softening his paths with bribery and generosity. Still, he couldn't shed his Korean origins completely. He believed in Korean shamanism. Each new year he held a "goot," a Korean shamanistic rite, where the *mudang,* a female shaman, warded off evil spirits and brought good fortune by dancing and hopping, in trance, on the cutting edges of long knives, speaking in tongues and prayers.

In 1945, World War II ended and broke the body and spirit of the Japanese. They limped home, and in no time, the Soviets moved in, and with them, the new wave of their home-grown Korean communist fighters. To be sure, the underground communist cells had already infiltrated Korea, stealthily weaving the network, expanding their members, paving the way for the Soviet army. Kim Il-Sung, the grandfather of the North Korean dictator, Kim Jong-Un, was one of the Soviets' top guerrilla fighters. The Russians appointed him the commander of the Korean communist party, although he barely spoke Korean, having spent most of his life in exile in China and Russia. The political situation quickly turned wildly unpredictable in Korea. The only thing everyone agreed on was the hatred for Japan and its people.

Grandpa, so used to wielding power, didn't react fast to the immediate dangers that were closing in. As he had always done, he trusted that money would buy the people he needed to buy. Politics may change, but the power of money was everlasting, it opened every door there ever was, was his firm belief. Aunt didn't share that trust. She'd been watching the fanatical communist rebels' movements all along. They were cunning. They spread like smoke, moved like shadows; you felt them but couldn't tell who or where they were. Your maid could be one, or your cook, or the gardener. They were bloodthirsty, made more brutal by watching the masters of cruelty and sadistic violence—the Japanese. Aunt knew they'd come for them, and swiftly, if not for political reasons, then for sheer envy; men killed for much less. But no matter how well Grandpa trusted and loved her, she couldn't convince him; her cool personality didn't lend itself to hysterical pleadings. So when Uncle, a southern aristocrat, no less, showed up, she saw her chance to escape.

Aunt hated the idea of marriage. It meant she must live under and for a man. She felt her destiny was running the family business, living not as an old maid, as people called her behind her back, but as the queen of her domain. A queen if you had power, if not, then yes—a spinster, a hag, even. She quietly packed their essential valuables, sewing money, jade, and gold into the clothes and into pouches that would belt around their waists.

On a humid summer morning in 1945 when the Japanese hadn't yet declared their official defeat and Aunt was still in her escape preparations, the underground communists raided Grandpa's company. He was incensed, not alarmed, and swore that heads would roll. But his anger never saw the day. The communists, some who were Grandpa's employees, barged into his office, and went on a blood orgy. They then dragged blood-soaked Grandpa to the top floor of his building and handed him a rag. At gunpoint, he was told to clean everyone's shoes, soles included, with his tongue. Room to room, floor to floor they took him around. He knelt in front of his employees' shoes, those shoes which, only that morning, didn't dare step on his shadow. When one faithful employee said no, and tried to help Grandpa up, the employee was shot on the spot. That afternoon, they took Grandpa to the middle of the town square with his hands bound behind his back, his head sticking out from a large, thick wooden board that sat on his shoulders. His employees were ordered to gather around him and chant the words written on the board, "Japanese Bitch," then stone him until his skull cracked. Not a single Japanese soldier or police officer came to intervene. Grandpa was then left on the spot for the hungry wild dogs that feasted on him past sunset.

Aunt's brother who was with Grandpa in his office was shot to death. The second brother, the Japanese Imperial Army officer, hadn't been heard from. The youngest brother, Han-woo, was home with tuberculosis, which was rampant. Luckily Aunt wasn't in the office. That night, Aunt, Mom, and Han-woo escaped through the backdoor with the help of their maids Aunt had bribed for their silence. Han-woo kept faltering, unable to walk, wanting to rest. Aunt carried his leaden weight with one arm and a suitcase with the other, while Mom carried the other suitcases, their ears and eyes on lookout for hostile movements and sounds. They walked the dark side streets, all the way to the train station and hid overnight inside an abandoned pastry shop near the depot. There were no pastries in the shop, cupboards smashed, rats everywhere. The Japanese family who owned it either escaped or was killed. Whenever Han-woo coughed blood into his handkerchief, Aunt covered him with her body, afraid of his noise echoing out to the empty streets.

Before dawn, as Aunt had planned, a man came and took them around the train station, across the tracks and into the last car, the caboose, with the train crew. By the time the train was moving, they no longer had a clean handkerchief for Han-woo, and blood darkened his teeth and lips. Again Aunt laid him, covering him up as best as she could from the crew's eyes. The train took forever, and from time to time, the crew jumped out to repair the damaged tracks ahead. Sometime later when Aunt and Mom woke up from their restless sleep, Han-woo was gone. Aunt confronted the train crew but they ignored her. Aunt persisted. Finally a crew member blurted out. "He was stinking to high heaven. He was dead and shit himself all over. We had to throw him off the train." Aunt didn't argue, she couldn't risk being thrown off, too. She held Mom close to her, to keep her from crying, but also to better hide their valuables. Huddled together, they rode and rode for what seemed like an eternity.

Aunt and Mom settled into a new life in Uncle's family home below the 38th Parallel that the Soviets and Americans eventually agreed would separate North and South Korea. That didn't last long. In 1950, a year after Kang-jin was born, the bombing started. America and the Soviets were fighting; America fought to free Korea, the communists to expand their rule. By the time the three-year Korean war ended, there wasn't much left standing on Uncle's land.

So Aunt moved to Seoul with Kang-jin on her back, my Mom and Uncle by her side.

Uncle who had never lifted a finger in his entire life, retreated into books. Aunt nagged him that if he loved reading so much, at least do something useful with it. So he studied Korean traditional medicine and eventually made himself a doctor. But he didn't feel comfortable taking money from his patients or talking about money, preferring to be above it all. Aunt fought with him, it riled her that he'd treat the poor for free and shun the wealthy. Uncle, unable to withstand Aunt's nagging but also unable to change his ways, changed his location instead and went back to his ancestral home.

With his brothers, Uncle tried to rebuild what properties still stood after the war, practising Korean medicine on the side. But people didn't want to live near the DMZ; why be the first to get killed when North Korea invades again? It was thought to be just a matter of when, not if. Although Uncle could never bring back his family's former glory, he comforted himself in his noble lineage. No one could destroy or take that away from him. He retreated into the past more and more, only wearing a Korean traditional hanbok that made him look old and dated especially when the whole country was getting into step with the western world. People no longer worshipped their ancestors like Uncle did—at least, not as much.

Aunt stayed in Seoul, taught herself tailoring and raised the family with her two hands, literally. Mom said that was when Aunt began cursing; it was her tonic.

• • •

Aunt fascinated and puzzled me. She had a dual personality; Aunt at home and Aunt at church. Even on her way to church, she often rapid-fired insults at Uncle's financial impotence. He simply walked on, expressionless, as if she were commenting on the weather. Lee looked equally unaffected, keeping pace with her. In-sook and I rushed ahead, embarrassed. But as soon as we got to the church, Aunt became composed, her voice light and in good humour. Every Sunday morning, rain or shine, in her Sunday best dress, she stood by the church door, handing out programmes, shaking hands with parishioners, giving special care to the newcomers.

The church was a remarkable place; everyone in it seemed happy and kind, joking and laughing easily, shedding their Korean seriousness, Aunt too. She welcomed anyone who walked in, even those hoping for a handout, a free lunch, perhaps. The church never turned anyone away. This must be what America is like, I thought—loving, charitable, trusting the good in others.

The church also meant music. It introduced singing in unison to Korea. Of course, the farmers often sang together while working in the fields, but it wasn't the same thing. The church singing was more intentional, serious, and with specific unifying messages. Church music also introduced the eight-note scale that afforded harmonising in various chords and their progressions. Women and men might sit in separate sections, men on the right, women on the left, but they sang hymns together. Gradually the church choir became a very important part of the church's success, as nothing touched people like music, especially human voices.

Although I was only eight, they put me in the adult choir. And I often sang solo while the collection baskets were passed around. Singing came to me as natural as speaking, only more memorable, more at home. While singing, I felt I was better than me, and there was more to me. Later, I became interested in other churches and their choirs. Churches had slightly different service hours so I visited others whenever I could. No church ever chased me out, and to my great joy, I found out that the bigger the church, the bigger the choir and more glorious the music. I loved Protestant hymns for their wonderful melodies and emotional messages. But it was in Catholic churches that I heard music unlike anything I'd heard before—mystical and unearthly, even the priest's chanting added to the exotic flavour. In the presence of music, I felt I became porous, as if music seeped into me. I didn't know the word "soul" yet then, but if I did, I would've said, "Music lifted my soul."

Chapter Eight

Two Korean soldiers flagged us at the checkpoint.
"Ah, Miss Kim's back. The sun can go home now," one soldier said.

"I'm sure you've got dozens of suns going in and out everyday," Mom said, laughing.

"Ahhh, but it's Miss Kim that we worship," he said, bowing deeply, theatrically. The three bantered on. Then one soldier said something to Mom, tilting his head towards me, but so quietly that I couldn't hear. All the while Mom held me close, smoothing my hair.

We walked on and Mom ushered me in to a large building. My immediate thoughts were how white, light and clean it was.

White curtains hung from ceiling to floor, end to end, dividing the dome-shaped hall into twelve equal parts, six on each side; a long corridor cut through the middle. High on the ceiling, rows of fluorescent tubes lit the entire hall, the colour of a crisp winter morning; what a contrast from home where the single lightbulb dangled from the ceiling, casting our ghostly shadows that followed our every move. Mom led me into her room where there were curtains flowing on three sides, a small window on the fourth curving wall. The room contained a large frame covered with thick blankets, a tall wardrobe and a tabletop cupboard; orderly, cosy and clean. How could it be so clean when everyone walked around inside with their shoes on? At home it was unthinkable. You just didn't walk into a room with shoes on. And how did the curtains stay so clean when people were parting them all day long to get in and out of their rooms?

Suddenly Mom lifted me up high and dropped me on the thick blankets over the long frame. I screamed, then burst into giggles and laughter. I felt like a little child again, rolling and rolling; such softness, like I'd fallen into a nest of fluffy bunnies. I'd never seen a bed before, we slept on the hard floor just like all our neighbours.

"I'm staying here, forever. I'm never going back," I shouted. Mom didn't say yes, but she didn't say no, either. She simply smiled. She knew that I knew this was only for the weekend. It took her three years to keep her promise, but she finally brought me to where she lived and worked.

From the bed, I watched her sort out my clothes, putting her belongings away, taking out the trash;

I never imagined she did these household chores like Lee or Aunt. To me, Mom was a perfection that walked and talked, impeccably dressed, always immaculate.

By the time we got out of her dormitory, it was late and the camp was deserted, but we went to her office as she had promised. She didn't actually have an office, but a desk in a long hall along with many other desks, some messy, mostly orderly, each stacked with files, yellow pads and a typewriter. Although this was the first time I'd seen a typewriter, I knew the importance of this intricate machine. Mom's ability to type fast on it was the key to her job, along with her English. I was surprised and proud to see my photo on her cramped desk. I was five in the image, sitting on an elaborately carved chair, fists clamped tight, my little round face gazing intensely into the camera.

Mom gently knocked on the door near her desk. A voice came from within. Inside, an impressively large man in a decorated military uniform sat behind a desk. He said something, I assumed in English. They spoke, then he rose up and came around his desk. Here was a man unlike any I'd ever seen before. An American more than twice as tall as me and three times wider. He stood erect in his massive frame. Bending his neck, he regarded me, as if to examine me. I looked down; we were taught not to meet the gaze of grown ups, as it was impertinent, but to look at the second from the top button of their shirt. As he was so tall, I focused on his belt buckle instead. But I had already taken him in.

He was a fearsome man; his large head with receding hair, cut very short; an arched nose like a predator's bill; thick brown eyebrows going straight across, almost touching. But Mom seemed comfortable, laughing her melting laugh, him laughing back, chatting as friends would. His hand touched her shoulder and kept it there. Mom blushed; I gripped her hand tightly, as if to guard her. He smiled and said something that made Mom hold me closer.

Mom's face was still flushed as we walked over to the side entrance of another steel corrugated dome building. This time, without hesitation, she banged on the door. To my surprise, Mr. Chang came out grinning, his white uniform splattered with grease and sauces. He scooped me up and nuzzled me with his chin as if I were a baby, which I didn't mind. "Lucky, lucky girl," he said, "Your mom talked about nothing but you all week."

I liked Mr. Chang, a wiry, little man with a goatee. Mom and he were close friends. I'd been to his home on a few Saturday afternoons with Mom. He lived with two sons in a tiny shanty not too far from Uijongbu. Before he got the job here, he was quite poor. He couldn't find work, couldn't feed himself or his children. They often took the long walk to the army base looking for food, sifting through garbage, eating whatever they could find, so hungry that sometimes even swallowing the cigarette butts embedded in it. That was where he met Mom, who was passing by. Soon, she was giving them leftovers and eventually found him a job working in the army cafeteria—the best thing that ever happened to him after the war, he said. I liked his younger son, Gombo-Oppa very much. He was the same age as Kang-jin. From the moment we met, despite the age gap, we played as if we were equal. He wanted to be a painter and taught me to draw which came in very handy for my paper-doll making.

It was Mom's ongoing promise that someday when she became rich, Mr. Chang would quit his job and do nothing but cook just for us. We'd live together in one big house. I knew this would come true. Mom kept her promises.

As we said goodbye, he handed us a large brown bag that gave off a delicious smell.

Back in her room, Mom spread out our dinner on the tabletop cupboard: Mr. Chang's roasted chicken, mashed potatoes, green beans, carrots, and a large slice of yellow cake with white frosting, which was my favourite. Mom said it was called limoncello cake. Much later, I rediscovered this cake in a modest restaurant in Tuscany. I got tearful as these days with Mom flooded and swirled in my mouth: an insignificant pleasure but significant, too, making my tongue as sensitive as a fingertip on braille.

"What's all this?" a voice said. I looked up and jumped. Poking in through the curtains was a waxy, yellow head, its mouth a chaos of twisted teeth. Then like some evil mask come to life, the curtains parted and in walked Mrs. Han.

"It's alright, you remember Mrs. Han, don't you?" Mom said calmly, touching my hand.

Mrs. Han came closer and surveyed our indoor picnic. "How you've grown, Ah-gha! Practically a young lady. So good to see you. I've missed you."

"Yes, Su-young is a first grader now," Mom said.

"Oh, you got her a name, too. Good for you! Eat, eat. Don't let me interrupt. Ah-gha-ya, or Su-ya did you say? Whatever, enjoy your stay. If you need anything, I am only a few steps away." She disappeared behind the curtains.

"Don't worry. She's just a co-worker. She can't hurt you. But don't go wandering around the hall. Stay in here, always," Mom warned.

Before going to sleep, Mom took me to the bathroom which was at the far end of the corridor, its door also made of curtains. Inside, the shower heads, sinks with taps, and toilet bowls lined the walls. We were all alone.

I tried to look away as Mom took off her clothes; I'd never seen her naked. Of course, I'd seen many naked women during the weekly scrubbings in our communal bath house: Lee's pink, bulging, bountiful flesh; Aunt's bony frame, her bosom like two flattened water melons; Mi-hae's flawless, slender body resembling a prancing young doe that the women never failed to gawk at. Mom's nakedness gave me a queasy feeling, but I couldn't turn away. Bent down to wash, she reminded me of a nude painting in Mi-hae's art book, with her pale, round arms by her ankle with a washcloth, the copious breasts spilling down, and her narrow waist exaggerating the voluminous hips. From one angle Mom was the vision of a goddess I held her to be, but from another, she made me think of a late summer peach, a bit overripe. I shook away the thought; it made her too human, too fragile. She was larger than life, grander, and nothing like my irritable, unhappy Aunt, nor the coarse, loud neighbourhood mothers.

I left the bathroom so Mom could finish her washing. Walking back down the long corridor, women were chatting in their rooms behind the curtains.

"Can you believe it? Kim brought her daughter here. She's got guts, bringing a kid. Who does she think she is!" It was Mrs. Han's voice.

"Don't you feel sorry for her? I do. She should've given that kid up long ago. It's still not too late. She can still put her in an orphanage and be done with it. That's what I'd do. She's too soft. How will she get a husband with that thing stuck on her hip?" another said.

"I don't care what she does with her kid. Just don't go breaking our house rules. We could all get into trouble. Just because the colonel favours her, she thinks she can get away with anything," said Mrs. Han.

A third woman said, "Well, not just the colonel. Can't you see the whiplash she gives every man in the camp? See how they goggle at her? The way she wiggles in that tight skirt? I once had a wasp waist like her. You should've seen me then!"

The women cackled.

"Seriously, she can't bring a child here. That kind of thing will give our camp a bad name, ugh." Mrs. Han said.

I laid next to Mom unable to sleep. Would she really send me to an orphanage? Should I ask her, confront her? No, I knew the answer. What did they know about me and Mom, these women, whose gossip and talk was as vulgar as Aunt's? They are just jealous because Mom's more beautiful than they are, more beautiful than any woman I knew, perhaps with the exception of Mi-hae. But somehow Mi-hae didn't count, she was still a student.

Mom seemed awake too. I slid in the crook of her arm and asked for a story, her childhood story. Unlike Aunt who loved telling us every glorious and gory detail of her past life, Mom never talked about hers. All she could remember was the horrible last days in Pyongyang and the escape to the South.

"Who is my father? Where is he?" I did it, I finally asked. It was a taboo subject, but I felt the time was right, here, with just the two of us. Mom said nothing. Silence dragged on.

"All I ever wanted was to be an actress. When you are an actress, everyone loves you," she said. I held my tongue. Aunt told me all actresses were harlots.

"I almost did become an actress," Mom said, almost to herself, then she went on, pausing at times, as if she were rummaging through an old chest of once treasured, now forgotten things. She said a man had stopped her in front of her academy where she was learning typing skills and English. Her schooling had been interrupted, but she still managed some middle school, some high school and even some college though she never graduated due to the wars and lack of funds. This man who stopped her said he was a film director and wanted to audition her, that she was the ideal female lead he'd been seeking for his new movie. He gave her his card. She was sceptical at first, there were men like him walking the streets offering young women opportunities beyond their dreams. But when she asked around, she found out he was genuine, and well respected too. She went and read for him. He said he had guessed right, she was perfect.

At that time, she was dating a young man who, at the age of twenty-eight, was to become one of the youngest members of the national assembly. "No, you can't become an actress," the young man had said, "not if we are to be married." He could never marry an actress and put his future at stake. It was either him or her acting. So Mom never went back to the director. But in the end, the young man didn't keep his promise of marriage. Like any well-bred Korean male heir, he obeyed his parents and married a woman of his own class they found for him. The director was Kim Ki-young, who later would become a legend in the Korean film world.

I wanted to know if this young politician was my father, but since she avoided my first question, I asked, "Did he give you the earrings you always wear?"

She didn't answer that either. We fell into silence again. Mom's breathing was now shallow and agitated. I felt her mind drifting away, most likely into her past that didn't include me.

The earrings in question were perfection for the details that took your eye; encased in fine gold, the oval water-blue transparent stones had an intricately carved pagoda, including its tasselled, tiered roof and a tiny person sitting cross-legged in the centre. Dangling down from Mom's graceful ear lobes, they were the ideal reflection of her elegant style.

The moonlight came through the small window. Eventually Mom's breathing slowed then became regular and she fell asleep. I sat up. There was a full moon lighting up the night sky. There was a legend about the full moon that told of a rabbit busily making a rice cake. The legend was that inside the full moon, the rabbit pounded his rice cake in a large mortar with a long pestle. I'd been frustrated by my inability to see that rabbit, let alone the pestle or mortar. My imagination didn't go that far. But tonight, I had all the time to figure it out. I couldn't waste this precious night sleeping.

The stillness and sameness of the night dulled me, the moon as mysterious as ever. I spooned against Mom's back, the heat from her body enfolding me like her silky scarf, my legs rubbery and weightless.

Someone shook me. I woke up. It was Mom. She said to get up and hurry, that we were leaving, right now. But it was only Saturday morning, not Monday. "No, no," I said. "I'm not leaving. You promised me!" Desperate, I wrapped myself around a leg of the bed. Mom yanked me up.

"Please don't make this harder than it already is."

"I am not going. I don't want to go back!" I was screaming and crying very noisily.

"What's going on? What's all the noise?" Mrs. Han walked in.

"Someone reported Su-young being here. I was warned to get her out, or else."

"Why don't you talk to your colonel? I'm sure he'll intervene."

"He's gone for the weekend" Mom said.

"That's too bad." Mrs. Han clicked her tongue. "Ahgha just got here. What harm can she do? It's only for a few days. Seriously, people have no heart! Shall I talk to someone for you?" she offered, but her eyes were laughing.

With my face flat against the window, I stared out of the bus. Whenever Mom tried to coax me closer to her, I held my body rigid, unyielding. I wanted her to know I was angry. To be chased out like that, how could she let that happen. She wasn't as powerful as I thought. Her brilliant glow I took for granted had vanished, just like that. She looked shabby now and it terrified me. But what hurt the most was that I might never go back to where she lived.

The bus bumped and lurched along through the endless fields of rice paddies, only the snaking irrigation ditches breaking the green monotony. A man pulled at his cow, but they barely moved, looking more like they were in a picture frame. The time was in no hurry either, favouring their speed. I wanted this bus ride to be over already, but also for it to go on forever as Mom was next to me, no matter what.

Mom pulled me to her again, I gave in this time. She held out her hand and opened it. Her pagoda earrings glinted in the sun. "These are yours to keep," she said, cupping them into my hand.

● ● ●

For ten full minutes, I sprinted through the streets, dodging oncoming cars, skilfully weaving through the pedestrians, falling, scraping my hands and knees, annoyed that my legs were too short and too slow, when my head was already at home with Mom.

Now that I was in school, I went through this routine every Saturday. Schools ended early on Saturdays, at noon to be exact, just about the time Mom came to visit. I hated missing her arrival but I was almost always late.

When I got home, Mom was in Aunt's shop already, talking with her, the air around them thick. "Go inside, grown ups are talking, your mom will be in soon,"

Aunt shooed me away. Mom agreed, nodding with a distracted smile, also wishing me gone. Something had changed since I got back from her camp. Her Saturday visits became sparse, now every other Saturday at best. No use asking her if she would be coming next Saturday. "Yes, of course, I wouldn't miss it for the world to see my daughter," she'd say. This time she was three weeks late and she had no time for me. I went back into the house, sullen. "I'll show her. I'll show her what it's like for her to miss visiting me," I told myself as I crammed myself into the bottom cupboard of the tall chest, my old hiding place, and shut the door from inside. I was folded from my knee to nose. I was resolved to keep quiet when Mom came looking for me: I'd let her suffer; I'd only come out when she got really scared thinking that I'd gone off and died. How she'd cry for me, asking me to forgive her, then she might even bribe me with a walk to the rotisserie chicken shop.

I waited, my ear stuck to the cupboard door. No sound. I dozed off then woke up. Still nothing. My legs hurt, my feet and back numb. I'd grown. The cupboard was no longer the cosy snug place it had been from three years ago but tight like a tiny box a magician squeezed himself into. I kept my belongings here; my paper-doll collection, my school bag, and Mom's earrings which I put in a small pouch made from Aunt's fabric scraps and then inside a tin box. When I first brought the earrings home, Mi-hae took them to the light and examined every detail, turning and turning, front, back, side, front, back, side. When she handed them back to me, her eyes were steely and thoughtful. Aunt clicked her tongue and shook her head, clearly feeling I was too young for such valuable things; another of Mom's foolish actions.

I was hungry and sore all over, the air inside the cupboard hot and stuffy. It felt like hours had gone by. I opened the cupboard door a smidge for air. The room rippled in golden waves from the mellow afternoon sun, the dust particles, trapped in the sun's rays, sparkled. I tumbled out. Mom had won. I would go to her.

Except there was no Mom, only Aunt at her sewing machine. "Where have you been? Your mom had to go, couldn't wait for you."

I keeled over, wailing with regret that I'd played hard to get!

"Stop that! Did someone die? What's the big deal? She'll come back next week. And don't you screech like a she-wolf. It's bad luck, I've got enough of that already. Do you want my whipping?"

I'd welcome her whipping, to snap me out of my self-pity. But she didn't and only kept on sewing.

A strong smell woke me up. I was in the main room. I'd fallen asleep in Aunt's shop and someone had brought me in. Lee was peeling cloves of garlic from a large basket of garlic bulbs and next to it sat a bunch of bright green chive stalks. I crawled over and put my head on her generous thigh. She crooned a song.

"Get up and help me peel this garlic. I have to make chive kimchee before I get the dinner ready."

But I didn't move, Lee didn't move. She ran her garlicky fingers through my hair over and over, mumbling a song. I put my face into the crevice between her thigh and her folded calf. It felt cool and welcoming.

Chapter Nine

Mom held up a stunning pale yellow dress with a green velvet rose over the heart. Laid on the floor were a pair of white shoes with chrome buckles and matching white socks, with fancy lace trim at the ankles. I'd never seen such an opulent outfit before, and it was for me. "We're going out for lunch," Mom said.

The taxi dropped us off in Myeong-dong, Seoul's most important, thriving commercial district. Famous for its dizzying neon sign displays, people said Myeong-dong woke up at sunset. Even in daylight, many signs were lit up, stacked one on top of the other so you could barely see the buildings themselves. I restrained myself from skipping about, feeling tingly all over, my toes wiggling inside the new slippery cotton socks. We'd been on Saturday outings before, but today felt particularly special.

We stepped into an imposing red arch with bold Chinese characters written in shiny black paint. The heavy wooden doors parted without Mom's touching them. Inside, ornate, gilded wall mirrors reflected what was happening in the room. In between the mirrors were panels of jade carvings depicting landscapes and human figures. Gnarled, almost prehistoric-looking magnolia branches stretched out from a large urn in the centre of the room, their magnificent white and pink blossoms touching the ceiling. The room shimmered from the sun reflecting off the cut glasses on the tables.

Two men in white suits ran towards us gushing, bowing. Then they pattered ahead, their arms held out, pointing at the steps down and led us to a round table by a window. Gold-rimmed dishes, tall drinking glasses, folded napkins in the shape of a bird, silver chopsticks and spoons were evenly placed on the white tablecloth that fell to the floor. The room glowed with happiness and anticipation. A few diners were already seated, elegant and comfortable in the surroundings. Suddenly I felt unsure. The Chinese restaurant near our home was a humble little shack, offering a few cheap noodle dishes that catered to day labourers and office workers, still a great treat for us whenever Aunt ordered a takeout.

With efficiency and ceremony, one man in a white suit pulled out a chair for me. I looked to Mom; she nodded for me to sit. I sunk into its plushness that swallowed me up. Another man, also in white, placed an extra cushion behind my back: "For the princess, so pretty and poised," he said without a hint of irony. He also placed a small stool below me so that my feet wouldn't dangle. I was embarrassed by all this fuss.

Mom was chatting with a waiter when the room suddenly hushed. All heads turned towards the door. A very tall and slender man sauntered into the room; an American, uniformed like the colonel at Mom's camp. Mom gave a short wave. He smiled and walked toward us. People's eyes followed him to our table and stared. Mom, without a thought to watching eyes, welcomed him, speaking animatedly in English.

He was the only white person in the room. Even sitting down, he was easily a head taller than everyone, and also like the colonel, his hair was shorn close to his skull. His blond head sparkled as if gold dusted. Suddenly he turned towards me. I was caught, I'd been staring at him but I couldn't turn away, his eyes captivated me—intense green eyes that you could see into, eyes so lively that they seemed to talk without words. Before this man, I mostly looked into dark brown eyes, those severe eyes that rarely smiled, but quickly judged and put me in my place. This man's eyes were serene yet playful, and I felt safe in them. In a funny lilt of barely understandable Korean, he said, "How are you? I've heard so much about you. I hope we will be great friends." He held out his large hand. Again, I looked to Mom; it was all wrong, grown ups didn't talk this way to me, let alone a foreign man, who towered over me like a giant, trying to please me, wanting to be friends. Mom was no help, she just smiled, looking very pleased. I didn't give him my hand.

The waiter asked what I wanted to eat, but the thick leather bound book he handed me was too intimidating, so I blurted out the first thing that came to my mind, "Black bean noodles!" The only Chinese dish I knew and loved. The waiter and Mom broke out into laughter as if I'd said something funny. Mom whispered, "Su-young-ah, restaurants like this, they don't make black bean noodles, that's street food. Can you . . ." but before she could finish her sentence, the waiter said, "Do not worry. I'm sure the chef will make an exception. We hope she won't be disappointed," smiling and bowing, he walked away. Where was I, how was all this possible? Everything was so simple and easy, people bending backwards to please me. Even in my dreams, I could not have make this up. But when the dish came, my face fell. What disappointment: a small dollop of noodles at the centre of a huge plate, all that empty space around it wasted. It'd be gone in three bites! Cautiously, I took a small bite and swooned. These were nothing like the noodles I knew. A mellow richness hit my nose first, the noodles glided into my mouth, chewy and silky, no greasy oil separating from the noodles like our neighbourhood takeout. Small bits of onions, potatoes and pork in the glistening brown sauce were tender but kept their distinct flavours, not the usual pool of mush. This noodle dish became the standard by which I judged all black bean noodle dishes from then on.

After lunch, we strolled along the lush green foliage surrounding the pond of now the famous Secret Garden in an ancient palace, Chang-deok Gung, in the heart of Seoul. The green-eyed man took many pictures of Mom and us with a camera that he slung on his shoulder. When we came upon a shady path along the palace wall, he offered me his hand. This time I gave him mine. His large fingers swallowed it up. I felt safe in them. Mom held my other hand. He was looking at her, his eyes laughing, his mouth all teeth, smiling. One of his upper teeth was crooked, just like mine. I told Mom about our matching crooked teeth. She told him. He laughed, Mom laughed and I laughed too. We laughed and laughed at our shared imperfection; it felt good, it felt warm, it felt like a belonging. As they held me up, I glided above the ground, my feet kicking the air. Then they swung me back and forth and I flew like a kite, anchored, yet free. I worked to keep calm, pretending it was always like this, that we were just on one of our normal Saturday afternoon strolls.

When we left the palace, Mom hailed a taxi for the green-eyed man. The lanky, handsome man with one crooked tooth lingered by the taxi, holding the door. He didn't want to get in. His eyes were squinting against the dappled sunlight. He leaned over and whispered something to Mom, pulling her closer to him. Laughing she pulled away, giving her head a quick tilt towards me, as if to say, the little one's watching. She ordered him to get into the taxi, which he did, grudgingly. Once inside the taxi, he lowered the window and held out his hand to Mom but his long fingers grabbed just air. She gave him a wave and her famous smile. She then talked to the driver, tapped the taxi door and the taxi pulled away. He stared back at us from the rear window, smiling and smiling, until the taxi turned the corner and was out of sight.

Mom and I took another taxi and got out at a stoplight near Si-jang. The green light blinked. Instead of crossing, Mom pulled me to the side and knelt down, our eyes on the same level. She looked nervous. She kept running her hands up and down my arms as if to warm me up.

"Su-young-ah. What did you think of him? Did you like him?"

I nodded, yes. I sensed it was important that I did. She parted her lips like she wanted to say more, but she only straightened the hem of my new dress.

"Su-young-ah, I have a decision to make, and your answer is very important to me, because you are very important to me. You know that, don't you?"

I felt afraid. Everything around us dimmed except her face, which seemed to have become larger all of a sudden, as if I was looking at her through a magnifying glass: the laugh lines, the fine peach fuzz that feathered below her widow's peak, the distinct pores on her nose and cheeks, the dried pink lipstick making vertical lines on her lips, especially as she puckered them and swallowed as if her mouth had gone dry.

"Su-young-ah, the man you met today, you said you liked him. How would you like it if he became your father? But, I promise, I will only marry him if you like him. If you don't, we'll find another way for us to live together. It'll just take a bit longer, but I'll do what you want. Wouldn't you like to live in America?"

I gave her a big nod, yes. I had expected something terrible. But America! America was where everyone dreamed of going.

"I am glad because there's no future for us here. I promise you, we'll live together, very soon. But for now, I have to go to America first. Just for a little while, till I get settled down. Then I'll send for you. Sometimes, we go weeks without seeing each other, don't we? But I always come to you, don't I? I promise, before you know it, you will be flying to me in an airplane . . ."

I tried to take in what she was saying, but she was shaking as if she was naked in an icy wind. Then I remembered; this was what Aunt was trying to warn me about this morning: "Your mom's going to ask you something very important. All you have to do is say, 'Yes.' Yes, to everything. Don't you give her a hard time. And whatever you do, don't cry. Don't get in the way of her happiness. Do you understand me?" I understood now. Mom wasn't asking for my permission but gently telling me what was already decided.

"Don't worry, Mom. Go. I want you to be happy. I'll be fine," my words came out evenly and simply. I thought, there, that wasn't so bad. But we all knew that going to America was like going to heaven. And once there, nobody came back. Don't think now, I said to myself, Mom's still here, and don't look sad, and see, how her beautiful skirt is getting soiled in the dirt, she needs to get up. Mom hugged me tight, and in her arms, I flew away again like a kite, but now flapping, the string broken.

● ● ●

There was no need, but Aunt pinned me firmly by my shoulders. We stood in the back, in the open waiting area of the airstrip, close enough to see Mom's white open-toed shoes walking up the steps to the plane. The distance was short enough that if I bolted from Aunt and ran to her, I could get one more hug. But I didn't. I could've screamed for her not to leave. But I didn't do that either. Aunt's worry that I'd make a scene was unnecessary; I stood placidly under her firm grip, looking almost distracted, as if I were dragged in for a goodbye to a distant relative. It was the only way to get through this. I knew my place. I couldn't throw a temper tantrum. Tantrums were for kids who were secure in knowing they could throw them.

Mom turned towards us one last time atop the plane's steps and waived with her rolled up magazine. Aunt whispered, "Smile. Show your smile. So that she can leave happy." I grimaced, wide, the only smile I had.

Mom looked lovely in her flowered cotton dress, the colour of a clean white soap, dotted with faint pink petals and green leaves. She wore a pair of large sunglasses that hid half her face, adding to her mystery. She looked like a movie star, a noble woman, a stranger, anyone but my Mom. Her being my Mom was just an idea in my head with, I thought, no substance to it.

A heavy wind billowed her dress, outlining her now protruding stomach. Although she never said anything about her pregnancy, I heard Aunt whispering to Uncle that she was rushing off to America to have her child born there. Watching her round belly, I realised that the baby inside would snip away at our bond; if it hadn't already, it would eventually, completely. Why didn't she tell me about the baby? By not telling me, she had separated me from her new life and her new family, so that I was left in her past. And what great luck for the baby, to be with Mom always, and to have a father too—the word, "father" itself a mystery. What I'd give to be that baby, even for a moment. But I was back here, caught in Aunt's grip. I was a burden at every turn; a burden to Mom, a burden to Aunt, and especially, most unbearably, I was a burden to myself.

Chapter Ten

A thin blue air mail letter with a foreign stamp mark came a month after Mom left. She had arrived safely in Los Angeles and from there, had travelled to a place called Seattle where she and her new partner would live. They'd made some stops along the way sightseeing. This country is so vast, she said, it goes on forever. She rarely came across an Asian face, but the pale-faced strangers treated her with such kindness, it never failed to surprise her. In Seattle it rained day and night, weeks on end, mists and fog wrapping her into melancholy, her mood swinging like a young branch in a storm but the baby kicking within anchored her.

We all pored over that flimsy letter and read it over and over, as if it contained some foreign magic. Mom didn't mention me, only that she'd write soon.

Then three more months went by and no letters from her. Worried, I asked Aunt what if we wrote to her. I said, "we," so I didn't sound self-important. I imagined it would take Mom three to four months, maybe six at most, to send for me. But somewhere deep down, I didn't believe it would happen.

"Give her some more time. She's still settling down, busy with the baby girl."

"Baby girl? We got a letter, then!" I shouted.

"No, just my hunch that's all," she said.

In the early days after she left, Aunt and Uncle talked about Mom often before they went to sleep. "Well, she doesn't really deserve that Yankee-saeki," Aunt would say. Yankee-saeki wasn't a nice word. She also called them, "Those stinking Yankee barbarians." She said they ate so many animals that meat-smell poured out from their armpits and their hairy and non-hairy holes. Another of her classics.

"She's too old for him, for one. Why, he's only a few years older than Kang-jin! But Mi-hae. Our Mi-hae would've been perfect for him—right age, much prettier, more deserving. If she were a decent and thoughtful aunt, she would have given him to Mi-hae. Then Mi-hae would be in America now."

As far as I knew, Mi-hae and the green-eyed man had never met.

"What about Ah-gha?" Uncle asked.

"Who knows? What can she say to his parents? 'Here I am, an old hag, a yellow old hag, and here's my bastard.' It's bad enough she's older than him. . . .Yes, yes, she gave me all the money, everything she had, but how long will that last us? I don't know what to do about Mi-hae's university. Well, we'll see what she does. We've got her daughter. She has to send money."

I didn't mind their disparaging remarks, as long as they kept talking about Mom. It made her real, it also reassured me that I wasn't just a charity case. The physical distance between Mom and me had always been vast. Even when she was in Korea, I never knew what my rights were as her daughter, even as we spent those happy Saturdays together. Aunt was my real world. So half hopeful, half doubtful, I lived day by day.

• • •

It was early November, five months and two weeks after Mom left. It was an unexpectedly warm day, as if summer had stolen in for a time. I came home from school, entering through Aunt's shop, as we often did to let her know we were home. There, standing by her sewing machine, Aunt was holding an unmistakable blue air mail letter, her head deep into it as she was near-sighted.

"A letter from Mom!" I yelled, running to her.

Aunt stopped me dead in my tracks with her "you simmer down" look. Then she calmly folded the letter and put it into her pocket.

Now what do I do? I looked at Lee, hoping she would rally for me, but she kept her head down and went on cutting the fabric.

Didn't I get to read it? I waited, hoping she'd change her mind. But the letter was out of our sight as if there had never been one. Aunt took down one of the curved sticks from the hook and drew a shoulder line on the fabric with her chalk.

"Looks like your mom, her husband, and the baby girl are moving to Virginia to live with her in-laws. She's pregnant again, hoping for a boy, this time," she said casually as if she was telling me about her humdrum day. "But mark my words, she'll never get a boy. She's got too much *ki*. Or I'll bet you he hasn't got it enough."

Koreans talked a lot about ki, a kind of inner energy, the inner force of a person. Aunt said that if the wife had too much ki, girls were bound to be born. It was also a slight on the husband, that he wasn't manly enough to give the wife a son.

Awkward minutes ticked by. My *nunchi* told me not to push, but I couldn't help it. "Did she ask about me?" I said.

Silence. Then she said, "Yes. She asked if you were behaving."

Just then, I could feel her mood changing so I didn't ask when I'd be going to America. I knew if I said one more thing, her fury would explode. She'd lash out, "Where did you learn to tag on a tail," meaning, where did I learn to talk back?

Chapter Eleven

It was summer 1968.

Squatting in the dark kitchen corner like a frozen bull frog, Lee hadn't moved since lunch. I sat next to her, my hand on her meaty arm, helpless: I had nothing to offer but to be sad with her; once she'd gone, I wouldn't have a single touch of comfort left.

Out in the yard, her dirty laundry sat in the mucky scummy water, some parts already stiffening under the blistering sun; a basketful of spinach and green onions withering too. By now, Lee should have finished her laundry, hanging it neatly on the clothes line near the wall, washing and preparing dinner, hurting our ears, belting out her love songs, usually off-key. Uncomplicated and all heart, Lee loved her life—at Aunt's home.

"Go get married before it's too late, Lee. No man wants an old maid," Aunt had said at lunch, wiping away eight years of Lee's devotion just like that, no regret or concern wrapped in that dismissal. She didn't even wait till lunch was over. Lee dropped her rice bowl in her lap.

"Mom," as she called Aunt, "don't make me go. Where can I go? This is my home. You're all I have. Please, I'll work harder. I'll eat less. Only, let me stay," she pleaded, her ruddy cheeks now a white sheet.

Although she moved slowly, Lee did any and all things for the family and for Aunt's shop, using her best assets—her physical strength and hard work—to earn her keep and security. Sobbing, she begged on her knees.

"I'm not your mom, Lee. Go and find something else for your life. You aren't cut out to be a tailor. You've no sense for fashion. You're sloppy; you can't draw a straight line, even ten-year-old Su-young there can sew better than you. You don't add anything to me by hanging around my shop."

We all knew, and Lee did too, why Aunt was letting her go. Since Mom left over two years ago, money worries consumed us; with Mom leaving, so went our steady income. Aunt couldn't afford Lee any more. Anything else she said was an excuse, her pride talking.

Adding to the burden, but to her intense joy, last year, Kang-jin got into Seoul National University, Korea's most prestigious institution. And this year, Mi-hae was accepted into Ewha Women's University, also a stellar school. They both received scholarships, but scholarships only covered tuition.

No matter how poor they were, students didn't work to earn money. It just wasn't done. The idea of a student taking a job didn't take hold until the American way of life changed it all, many years later. Still, swallowing his pride, Kang-jin found a job as a tutor. This lessened Aunt's money worries somewhat. Thankfully, Aunt didn't have to worry about In-sook and me for another couple of years; we didn't pay tuition until middle school.

Like Aunt and Mom, Lee had also escaped from North Korea when she was twelve. During the war and while escaping, she lost her parents and baby sister. All alone, Lee tracked down a distant relative who lived in an obscure little fishing village at the tip of south east Korea. There, besides taking care of her ocean-hardened uncle, his mute wife, and their four young children, Lee worked in their two-table waterfront snack bar, with nothing to look forward to but to marry a fisherman, chosen by her uncle, if there were any eligible men still left. Women greatly outnumbered them. Wars ate men.

Weekends glued themselves to weekdays, indistinguishable from one another. No exclamation point marked a Thanksgiving Day, New Year's Day, certainly not her birthday; months and years slithered by. Lee's young blood wanted something different. She didn't know exactly what, but something different from this life by the sea. She kept that vague hope in her pocket, taking it out at nights, shining it, trying to figure out what she wanted, but her brain stayed muddled, except to let her know that it longed for Pyongyang, her home city. Then, one day, my Aunt and Uncle brightened her snack bar. They had come for fresh sea air and raw sea-food—clams, mussels, oysters, sea pineapples. Aunt's favourite was sea cucumbers; she liked them alive, their stumpy slippery bodies still wriggling while Lee chopped them into pieces on the cutting board. Dipped in hot sauce, sea cucumbers crunched in Aunt's mouth, ocean juice squirting out with each bite.

Lee, so awed by Aunt's blinding city glamour, put out more raw fish than she asked for and glued herself to Aunt. And Aunt, in a moment of sentimental tenderness for her hometown, also Pyongyang, took her in, as part housemaid, part apprentice in her tailor's shop. Since then, the only thing Lee had ever wanted was to be good enough to work side by side with Aunt in her shop. She never spent the money Aunt occasionally gave her, never took a day off, moulding herself as part of the family, eating the same food, sleeping in the same room, even going to church together.

I nudged Lee again. I couldn't undo Aunt's dismissal but wanted to cheer her up. "Come on, Lee. You've got to get up. Your legs will go numb. Look. Look out. It's raining, and the sun's blasting too. 'It's foxes getting married day,' you said. 'It's a lucky day' you said. Good things are going to happen!"

She didn't budge.

"Come, Lee. Let's go for a walk. Get some fresh air.

I've got a new place you'll love. There, you can figure out what to do."

Although Lee was much older than me, older even than Kang-jin, she was, in some ways childlike, easy to delight, easy to distract. But nothing I said so far had worked. So I tried what she loved hearing—my stories, made-up things, and this one hadn't an ounce of truth in it, since I was just as badly off as she.

"Lee, when I go to America, I'll invite you. You'll have your own room right next to mine. We'll sleep on a plush bed, so large that you'll get lost in it, and clothes, beautiful, fancy clothes of latest fashion, a room full of them. You can go to school if you want or get a job at a tailor's shop, then open your own shop. You'll be rich. They say you can do and be anything you want in America. When the winter comes, you'll wear a fur coat, not just on the collar, skimpy like Aunt's, but the entire coat made of fur, so soft and silky that your hand will slide right off, like on sesame oil. You'll look so beautiful, breaking the hearts of many men. We'll go to the opera to hear Maria Callas. Have you heard of Maria Callas? She is the greatest soprano ever, in the whole wide world. She lives only for music and love. When people hear her sing, they weep and scream from too much emotion they never felt before. Everywhere she goes, people throw rose petals at her feet. And after the opera, we'll go to a fancy Chinese restaurant and have them make us black bean noodles, the best on earth . . ."

"You do go on," Lee said finally, "where's this place you're talking about? Let's go."

We crossed the Mapo Boulevard away from the old Methodist church where In-sook and I used play. The new Presbyterian's massive front iron gate was locked up, but I guided a hesitant Lee through the small side door and we walked up the short curved hill that led to expansive, well-groomed grounds. From this open field, the church came into full view. Majestic and awe inspiring, it stood on an even higher plain than where we were. The only way to the church building was by walking up the endless stone steps, like a stairway to heaven. We trudged on. Lee was soaked through, her thin, sweaty hair matted to her scalp, breathing hard from the unexpected exercise. When we got to the top and faced the church's arched front door, I pushed her for one final effort, to make a sharp right turn around the church. Then after catching her breath, Lee looked up and gasped; it looked like the entire city of Seoul was laying at our feet, and we were standing on top like giants. In reality, it was just a wide view of our Mapo District. Far in front us, we could see the mountains: Namsan, the heart of Seoul, and farther up, the faint, undulating lines of Inwangsan, and farther still, Bukansan disappearing into the sky.

Lee's face brightened, her small eyes wide open, all fired up. She let out another long, freeing sigh. I cupped my hands around my mouth and gave a loud holler. Lee followed, her lungs letting out a thunderous sound. She hollered again and again. Lee was back to herself, more than back to herself. I held her hand and she squeezed mine.

"Do you want to try something really delicious?" I asked. Nothing made Lee happier than food: the idea of eating, when she was about eat, while she ate and then thinking about eating again.

"Watch," I said and bending down, I grabbed the first grasshopper in sight. They were everywhere if you looked carefully; on the blades of grass, pretending to be part of it, on bald patches of earth, pretending to be part of that, jumping away when touched.

I showed Lee how to catch them by pinching their backside with the thumb and index finger. If one hopped away, it was easy to follow it. They didn't hop far, and rarely flew away. Once caught, it was best to pull off a wing and a leg or two so that it couldn't jump away and then stash it in your pocket.

When we had gathered enough of them, I dug a small hole in the ground using a sharp stone. Then I laid some dry straw at the bottom of the hole, placed the grasshoppers on top, making sure they didn't hop away again and covered them up with more straw. Then I lit the straw with a match and shielded the flame with my cupped hands to keep it going. It was always good to have some matches handy as using two stones to get a fire going took a lot of effort. When the fire had died down, taking care not to burn my fingers, I took out the roasted grasshoppers, their bodies shiny from burnt fat.

I gave Lee one to taste. Although squeamish at first, she followed my lead and put it in her mouth. Her eyes rolled, surprised at the juiciness and crunchiness, tasting something between roasted chicken and roasted chestnuts. We were happy, munching on grasshoppers. Then following the smoke, the church groundskeeper ambled toward us, and rich with roasted grasshoppers in our pockets, we ran away like bandits.

Dusk settled, the alleyways darkened. But before turning the corner to our backstreet, Lee stopped and held my hand, suddenly looking serious. "Ah-gha-ya," she still called me Ah-gha; much tenderness and love were in that calling, "I've got something to tell you. I'm sorry I kept this away from you all this time, but your aunt would've killed me. But now I don't care. It's one thing I can give you." She took a long breath and looked around the alleyway, as if we were about to commit a crime.

"Your mom's been sending letters all along. I'd seen the mailman bringing those blue mailers to the shop many times. I am sure they're all from her. So don't be so sad, carrying on every night, crying into your pillow. Your mom will send for you, one of these days. But when we go home, you can't let on. You don't want your aunt to kick you out, too. You stay till you find your way to your mom."

I sank down.

I thought I'd throw up.

Chapter Eleven

Next morning, when we got up, Lee was gone, taking only the small bundle she brought with her eight years ago. She didn't wait for the new dress Aunt promised.

Chapter Twelve

Although still morning, the cubbyhole was already suffocatingly hot and steamy: the heat bore down through the roof and rose up from the kitchen below. I was lying on my stomach, the only way to stay in the cubbyhole for any length of time. You could sit in the centre below the apex of the sloping ceiling, but only just by bowing your head. The cubbyhole had one small window facing the yard which let in the light, but never any air as it was nailed shut. No one came up here in the summer, like now, because of its stultifying heat, or in winter because it was freezing cold. There was nothing much of value up here either: discarded winter blankets, old clothes, old 'don't need-em but can't throw-em away' things, like Mom's dated and worn-out American magazines, though these were still very much alive for me. How many times had I leafed through the pages, imagining Mom's life in

America; her making dinner in that beautiful indoor kitchen equipped with a sink and sleek taps; chopping vegetables on a long clean work top. And her husband sitting on a luxurious looking couch, reading a book and from time to time, glancing at Mom, full of affection. Or him out on their lawn—vivid green and evenly trimmed—with the baby on a swing, and the older girl running circles around them, giggling and yelping. So much happiness inside that white picketed fence.

But today, I wasn't in the cubbyhole to daydream about Mom, but to hide.

When I was little, Kang-jin and Mi-hae used to play pranks on me by locking me in this cubbyhole, then cackling like hyenas, they whispered through the door, "The ghosts are coming. The headless, blood spewing, hungry, angry ghosts are coming . . . looking for you . . . looking for ugly little monkey like you . . ." then stomping out to let me know I was all alone. I'd nearly faint from all the ghost stories jumping around in my head.

Ever since Lee told me about Mom's letters, I'd been consumed with trying to find them, but it was impossible. Schools were closed for summer vacation, everyone was home. Even Kang-jin came home for a week. Most of the year, he lived in the home of two middle school boys, tutoring them so they would pass the high school entrance exams, which would then pave their way to a good university. From time to time, he came home for a quick visit, to check on Aunt, to bring her little treats—melons in early summer, a bag of hot roasted chestnuts or sweet potatoes in winter, concord grapes (also Mom's favourite) in early autumn, and even managing to force a little money into her protesting hand. Uncle had recently gone back up north, so he wouldn't be home again for a month.

Today, I'd have all morning and afternoon to myself. After the church service, everyone would have lunch there, then Aunt had her elders' meeting, In-sook, her Bible study, and Kang-jin and Mi-hae would be off to see friends.

So as the house was empty of people, I went downstairs.

My first stop was Aunt's shop. I lifted all her pattern cutouts, swept through each stack of fabrics with my hands and searched under her worktable, the bottom of her sewing kit, and the drawers next to the sewing machines. No letters here.

Next, Kang-jin's old room which was small, so it was a quick search through his old books bundled in batches and stacked up high against one wall, a chest of drawers with Mi-hae's belongings occupying the other wall. Her books and notebooks piled up neatly on her clean desk. Nothing here either.

I made a stop in the kitchen too, just to make sure but found nothing.

The last place was our large main room with the tall chest. Aunt's clothes and belongings took up half that chest. I went through them carefully, every drawer, top to bottom. Nothing. Lunch time was long past now and I was exhausted and hungry. I lay down and retraced my steps to see where and what I might have missed. I would check Aunt's purses in the drawers and the stacks of her papers one more time soon after a short rest. Then I drifted off.

And I dreamt, not of Mom's letters, but of something noxious, something clammy and unpleasant slithering by my face, and moving down to my chest. My head was hot and thick. I tried to shake myself awake, but my body wouldn't respond. I couldn't open my eyes, my eyelids felt like they were sewn together. The slimy touches became more specific, grubbing at my chest. I yelled and kicked, but no sound came out, my limbs didn't move either as if frozen. Then a sharp pain on my nipples shocked me awake, they were being pinched and twisted. I tried to get up, but something hard, an elbow, dug into my collarbone. A face I couldn't see was above me, the arm stretched out, hand on my stomach, groping further below. I tried to pull myself up. The elbow banged my cheek against the floor; it hurt like being crushed and I screamed. The elbow then jammed into my mouth. I bit it as hard as I could, but the other hand was already inside my pants. I crossed and twisted my legs to it shake off. Then a whole chest crashed down on my face. I kicked and shoved, wanting air. Just then, everything stopped. I was simply let go. The feet scuttled away, the door opened and shut. Then I heard the reason why. Mi-hae and Aunt were chatting in the yard.

"Oh, Kang-jin-ah, what are you doing home? Weren't you seeing a friend? Where are you running to? Are you coming home tonight?" Mi-hae yelled after him.

I crawled to the cubbyhole door and clambered up the three steps. I threw down as many things as I could get hold of against the door, winter blankets, pillows, clothes, piling them up to block anyone from coming in.

It felt good to curl up with nothing touching me. I rocked myself to slow the shaking. I tried not to think, but the earlier scenes played in a slow motion, shot by shot, panic by panic, churning over and over. Then something happened: I was floating above my body, looking down at myself. It was strange, but it didn't feel bad or scary, except I didn't like what I saw: I looked like a shrimp, no longer the full size, but shrunken and curled up, quite dead, from the sizzle of a frying pan. I didn't want to go back into my body. I hovered a bit longer, then went out of the small window that didn't open. I could see everything—myself, the cubbyhole, the yard, the roofs, the streets. I was weightless, time-less, without feeling.

Dusk soon covered everything, beckoning the mysterious night with its unknown dangers. Time to go home. My thoughts swirled around; should I tell Aunt what happened? Would she believe me or blame me? Why did this happen? Mi-hae said I was a bad seed; am I giving off some mean, nasty odour that turns people violent? Why did he do such a thing? Did it really happen or did I just dream the whole thing?

One thing became clear. I couldn't tell Aunt and definitely not In-sook. So then the only thing I could do from now on was to be careful, very careful. No one needed to know what happened; I will hide my faults, be watchful of Kang-jin and stay away from him. I will have to go on; there's my school, my friends, music, and Mom and her letters, and the possibility of her getting me to America.

I sunk back into my body in the cubbyhole.

Chapter Thirteen

Aunt never left her purse just anywhere. If she was in the shop, it was right by her sewing machine, if in the house, it was in the middle drawer of the chest. Of her many purses, this one was her current favourite. Its generous size caught my interest: large enough to fit her Bible, hymn book, and other essentials, why not Mom's letters? Even if she threw away the old ones, couldn't a recent letter or two be in that purse? Just now it sat by the small door connecting to Aunt's shop; she was either going somewhere or coming back.

Cautiously, I peeked into the shop, Aunt wasn't there, the shop door locked from inside. I quickly ran around to see whether she was in another part of the house. But the house looked empty. I rushed back into the main room and quickly opened the purse. A chaos inside, everything was thrown in together. I leafed through the pages of her Bible and shook it, then the hymn book. I took out her handkerchiefs, a clean one and a soiled one, a notebook, and her money pouch.

"I knew it. You're just a dirty common thief!" Mi-hae hissed, snatching away the money pouch and the purse. "I'm not surprised. A sponger, and that's not enough, you're stealing, too. You will pay for this!"

It quite looked like I was stealing money. But I couldn't tell her I was looking for Mom's letters, that would be a major crime against Aunt, even worse a sin.

Mi-hae sat down, her small porcelain face flushed deep pink. Despite her struggle to look calm and in control, her fingers twitched as did her feet. She said she'd make a deal. If I met her demands, all would be forgotten, she wouldn't say a word to Aunt.

Her demands were either I give her my Mom's earrings, or accept ten lashes and write an apology letter. Not just any apology letter, but like a child being disciplined, I was to write, "I apologise, I will never steal again," one hundred times.

I thought I'd rather have my hand chopped off than give her Mom's earrings. The second option was unbearably humiliating.

"Didn't you hear what I said? What's it to be? I don't have all day," Mi-hae slapped the floor for my attention. Losing patience, she got out Aunt's whip and swept it above her head, ready to strike down at my bare legs. Then I began to scream: a long, crazed howl that went on and on.

A tremendous burning inside overtook me, ready to explode. I felt raw. I was looking at Mi-hae, but I didn't see her. Everything went white except for the frantic madness inside. I wanted that madness to burn me up. I howled again and again. My eyes were ablaze, my jaw twitched uncontrollably. Mi-hae fell backwards, terrified. I kept screaming and howling. I felt monstrously powerful. I screamed at the world, at what Kang-jin did, what Mi-hae could do, then the scream turned inward: I was screaming at myself, for being born bad, for having no home, no one, no me. I didn't know why I was here in this world. I didn't know how to get rid of my ugly self. When I had no more scream left, I growled, pacing right and left. I wasn't a person anymore. If Mi-hae made one wrong move I would have attacked and bit her, killing her or me. Nothing mattered. Mi-hae ran out, screeching, afraid.

I fell to the floor. Thick, juicy, red balls dripped down from my nose. It was magnificent to see the dark red blood splattering on the yellow floor. It was satisfying, too, as if all the vile, rotting things were pulsing out of me. I went out to the yard, put my head under the spigot and pumped the handle. The shock of cold water jolted me, and I kept on pumping the handle. I stood up, drenched, my chest cleared and calm. I was no longer afraid of Mi-hae. And if Aunt wanted to punish me, I was ready. She'd have to answer for Mom's letters she'd been hiding these last two years.

Later that evening, Aunt called me to her shop.

"Yes, your mom sends letters. Not often. But *to me,* you understand. They are for me, between me and my sister, who *I* raised!" Then softening, she said, "Su-young-ah. I'll be honest. It's going to take some time before she can send for you. She's got two kids, her young husband is back in school. They're living with his parents. You thought she went to some paradise? You think America's paved with gold? No, she can barely send me money she promised. She can't send for you till they can live on their own.

You are my blood. I promised to take care of you, and I will, no matter how long it takes. But you have to trust me and stop nosing around my things. I won't have it. It won't be just a talk the next time. If and when she's ready for you, you'll be the first to know. She hasn't written to you because she feels bad. She knows you are fine, because I told her so. But if you want, I'll let you write to her, but promise you won't badger her. It'll only make her life more difficult. Let her be. Let her live her life. You are young, with a full life ahead of you. For now, you just study and trust me. You'll understand better when you get older. Time and patience will take care of everything."

I went from Aunt's shop through the front to avoid Mi-hae inside. The street was bright with the neon lights and display windows all lit up, defying the falling night. I walked and walked. I wasn't sure how much of what Aunt said was true. But my desire to get to Mom's letters persisted, even if just to see her handwriting.

Good to her word, Aunt let me add a few words to her letter to Mom. No desperate pleas or longings— she'd have smacked me for having no sense of things. Sometime later, Aunt said she received the letter from Mom, but it only said she was pregnant again.

I kept up a happy front and waited for the right time to look for the letters. When fear or fretting affected me, I touched Mom's earrings. They soothed me, like worry beads.

I enrolled in middle school in January 1971. Aunt somehow was able to provide my tuition fees.

Chapter Fourteen

Yumi poked my ribs with her pencil, then pointed to the window. All eyes lit up, heads turning to the window. "Wow!" someone said. Mr. Bae, our maths teacher, tapped his ruler for our attention, but he, too, was taken by the display outside: candy sucker-sized snowflakes fluttering down from the sky; a heart-thumping-let's-go-mad-for-a-while kind of snowfall. It was for the elderly to worry about another ferocious winter ahead; for us, it was simply exciting, if for no other reason than it meant a change, something different for a day, an excuse to let out our pent up, thirteen-year-old energy that seemed to gather much faster than we were able to expend it. There was a saying that if you opened a new business on the first snow, you'd prosper; if you went on a blind date, it was a destiny; if you bought a lottery ticket ... , the superstitions went on and on. Even if these old wives' tales were only fantasies, we welcomed them. My classmates looked longingly at the window and then at Mr. Bae, their eyes pleading: "Please teacher, let us out, please, please."

"Alright. Lunch!" Mr. Bae gave in, a full ten minutes early.

Classmates bolted out, and just as quickly a chill gathered in the room. I looked at Sook-ja, the other one who didn't go out. Actually I looked right past her as if she were part of the classroom furniture, a desk or chair; she was an outcast. I walked over to the large standing stove in the centre of the room to warm myself. Ninety-eight bento boxes were piled up neatly around the stove since the first break this morning. This was how we ate a warm lunch: during each break, classmates took turns rotating the tin bento boxes so that everyone got their lunches warmed, not too burnt for some, not too cold for others. And the food inside got cooked, some boxes more than others and the raw kimchee in them cooked too, mellowing its flavour, sending out mouth-watering aromas, making us drool, testing our patience.

I guessed ninety-eight bento boxes because we had 100 classmates in the room. Some brought two layered boxes but I didn't bring lunch. The other missing bento box would be Sook-ja's. Neither of us brought lunch everyday. Like me, she had a difficult time at school and home. But it was worse for her. She didn't have a Mom like mine to dream about, who will someday send for her. Sook-ja had to care for her sick mother and her little sister and brother. She was also the shopper, the cleaner, and the cook and she bent to her father's beatings whenever he got drunk. But parents beating their children or teachers hitting students was normal discipline, so we didn't worry much about her bruises, except as good gossip. You could spot Sook-ja easily in the corridors or in the classrooms, although that was the last thing she would've wanted. She sat hunched over by the wall, avoiding the attention of teachers. She walked head down, never standing tall, exasperating our gym teacher, whose mantra was: "Suck in your stomach, stand up straight and you'll never have a back problem when you're old," as she smacked us with her ruler on our stomachs, shoulders, and backs till we stood as straight as her stick. When Sook-ja passed in the hallways, she kept her limp body close to the wall, as if to apologise for taking up space or perhaps to ask the wall for support. She didn't have a single classmate close to her. No one wanted a friend who dripped with sadness and neglect; no one noticed when she skipped school, except during roll call.

I also skipped school, but I wasn't an outcast, at least I didn't feel like one. I knew some teachers were forgiving because I excelled in music and art. I had a small gang of friends and a real friend in Yumi. She and I had attended the same elementary school and now, the same middle school.

Why was it that when one part of you got warmed up, the rest of you felt the cold even more acutely? My hands were warm, but my feet and back were freezing as if I was leaning against a block of ice. I turned round and round in front of the stove like a rotisserie chicken, hoping to warm my body, watching my classmates outside. Yumi and the classmates were spinning and spinning, with their arms stretched wide, tongues sticking out, tasting snow, laughing, yelling, running around, making themselves crazy like puppies seeing snow for the first time. Yumi beamed at me, waving, then ran up to the window, banged on it, her face close to the frigid glass, her nose squashed, eyeballs crossed, making a clown face, begging me to come out. I laughed and waved back. But I couldn't go out: it wasn't the cold; it was my sole flapping shoes, my coat riddled with holes, and bare hands that my classmates would've noticed. Already, I had learned to walk artfully, keeping my steps close to the ground, but without dragging, to lessen my shoe soles flapping like yammering mouths. Yumi backed away and aimed a snowball at me as if to throw it at the window, but she did a quick turn and threw it instead at Mr. Bae, who was standing on the entrance steps with other teachers. It hit him smack on his chest. Daring! Mr. Bae looked at his sweater, then at Yumi. He shook off the snow, stepped down and walked towards her. Everyone stopped dead, dread on their faces. Mr. Bae bent down, made a large snowball and threw it right back at Yumi. Yumi yelped, a crazy, happy yelp. Any remaining reserve they had was wiped away and a frenzied snowball fight began; it looked like one gigantic, swirling, snow storm.

Yumi had a crush on Mr. Bae, although he seemed rather ancient to us, already thirty years old. But not just Yumi: everyone went on and on about his light brown hair, matching light brown eyes, freckles on his nose and cheeks—very unusual for a Korean, also exotic and so appealing. And most impressively, he was a Seoul National University graduate. What greater attraction for serious-minded young Korean schoolgirls than a genius who had walked the grounds of Seoul University! But our crush on him cooled somewhat after an incident that some of us witnessed which, by the next morning roll call, everyone whispered about.

After each school day, it was the students' responsibility to clean the classroom. After cleaning, some lingered on, chatting and studying. For those of us who couldn't afford to go to the night academies, the quiet, empty after-school classroom was the best place to study and bond by sharing novels or even magazines, until the school guard chased us out. Magazines, expressly printed for young people, were not allowed at school for one reason: their wildly popular serials, stories of forbidden love—between students! If found out, you'd be severely punished. Adults and teachers acted as if we didn't indulge in such fantasies, that we lived only to study and study all our waking hours. They were not wrong as most of us did.

On one of these after-school hours, we heard a teacher yelling, then a series of whacking sounds. We rushed out, following the sound. It came from the teachers' hall, one floor down. The teachers' hall was empty except for Mr. Bae and a student. Crouched outside the hall, we peeked in through the window. Mr. Bae was flogging a student with his long ruler, all the while screaming at her. He hit her legs, shoulders and her behind. When his ruler broke in half, he slapped her with all his might. She fell. He kicked her, yelling at her to get up. She did. He hit her again, circling around her, watching her. She didn't cry out, just stood there, taking the beating. It went on and on. We couldn't make out what it was about. What gross offence could she have committed?

Teachers gave corporal punishment, often and casually, sometimes a single smack on our head with a book, but other times more severely. Then it was a measured mode of discipline, letting us know how many lashes we'd get or how many minutes or hours we'd have to stand in the hallway. We never passed by a teacher without a deep bow. They had absolute power to discipline us in any way they saw fit, but they mostly paid attention to students who they thought really mattered. Parents regularly came to school bearing gifts and lunches for teachers, often sticking an envelope of money inside the package, all to get their kids better treatment, better education. Mr. Bae, for example, would never flog Sook-ja very severely as she wouldn't matter to him.

What went on between Mr. Bae and that student was excessive beyond the normal punishment and had a different tinge to it, something dark, but that we couldn't quite pinpoint. We never found out what it was all about either, or to which class the student belonged. If other teachers knew about the beating, we weren't privy to the truth. When Mr. Bae came to our classroom the next day, he was the same witty teacher who made us laugh but our liking for him had somewhat diminished.

The snow storm gave no sign of letting up; the windows went white like the inside of a milk bottle, classmates barely visible. With only fifteen minutes left until the next class, crimson-cheeked and dripping-wet classmates lumbered in, grabbing their bento boxes by the stove. And just as quick, the room came back to life. Bento boxes clanged. Metal chopsticks made their tinny tingling sounds since well-off classmates boasted silver chopsticks, a status symbol that came down from ancient times when our emperors believed that the silver utensil turned black when it touched poison. Someone shouted, someone hollered back, others grumbled, laughed, whispered, threw things. We middle school girls were not demure young ladies, but wild and noisy creatures.

Yumi opened her bento box. Two perfect, round golden fried eggs glistened on top of her steaming rice. Other compartments held sautéed spinach, fishcake cooked in onions and carrots, burdock roots simmered in soy sauce and sugar. In her other bento box, bright red and green, round-cut cucumber kimchee were in neat rows, like a kaleidoscope.

I knew Yumi would offer to share her lunch with me, again. She had seen my life change over the years: from the happy days with Mom to now—coming to school without lunches, without proper gear for classes. She stood by me no matter.

I'd been debating whether to stay or skip out. The art class was next. It was my favourite class if we were drawing objects like the white plaster busts in the art class room, or a vase of flowers with crayons or pencils. But it became a dreaded class as we started on some fancy projects involving an embroidery set that you had to buy from the art store because school didn't provide art material. I knew the usual punishment: Miss Hong, our art teacher, either made you stand in the corner for being forgetful, not respecting her class, or she'd just ignore you and let you stew in your seat for weeks while your classmates carried on. Being treated as an outcast was worse than being left alone.

I skipped out of school. Leaving early without a teacher's leave slip was a risky act but in the falling sheets of snow, I got out unnoticed.

The street was quiet. People hurried on, their shoulders hunched up to their ears. A shopkeeper poked his head out, contemplating quitting for the day. Ignoring my growling stomach, I walked towards the public library, only twenty minutes away. I was hungry, always hungry, a constant presence. Although there would be ramen noodles at home, just thinking about it made my hunger worse. Aunt bought the cheap and filling ramen a case at a time. I sometimes chewed it raw like a savoury snack while studying. But these days, after eating it day in and day out, my stomach revolted and threw it back causing intense stomach aches during and after.

Not long after Lee left, Aunt stopped buying rice by the bushel like we normally did, as did our neighbours. We now bought rice in small bundles, one bundle lasting a week. When that was gone, we had ramen. Occasionally, Aunt sent me out to buy a small bag of rice, enough for one dinner. She was too embarrassed to go herself. "You are just a kid, they won't laugh at you," she once said.

On one occasion however, I failed at this small mission. It was monsoon season and on my way back from the store, rain poured down without warning. I protected the rice bag in the crook of my arm, shielding the top with my other hand. But it was a steep downhill, and I slipped and fell. My paper bag flew out, kernels of rice splattering, rolling down on the soggy wet dirt, our dinner disappearing right in front of my eyes. I was horrified. I got on my hands and knees, chasing after rice kernels that ran in all directions.

When I got home, the expected punishment from Aunt didn't come. She only sighed at the sight of a wet, torn bag with some muddy rice kernels I had managed to gather up. I washed them carefully, separating them from the dirt and gravel. It was a small dinner that night.

That same night, when everyone had settled into their sleep, I took out Mom's earrings. I knew every detail; permanently embedded in my mind with no chance of ever forgetting even if I never held them again. I crawled over to Aunt and tapped her hand. She turned to me, her eyes saying *what's wrong*. I put the earrings in her hand. She stared at them then at me. She didn't say anything but slowly closed her hand. Now they were gone from me for good. A little while later, I heard something I had never heard before: Aunt whimpering into her pillow.

Unlike In-sook who studied as if our poverty energized her, I shrank from study. I couldn't concentrate on school work. It was relentless. One missed homework, one skipped class—repeat that a couple of times, and you fell into a pit of academic darkness while your classmates sprinted forward at their morning and night academies, reinforcing what we'd learned, and studying ahead of what school would teach us that day. So, I hid in the public library where no one knew me or my poverty, where I could live in the made-up world of novels, compensating for my falling grades by seeking out difficult books my friends had never heard of. In doing so, I felt smart and worldly. And who could say I wasn't? The library didn't set exams. But deep down I didn't fool myself; I knew I wasn't smart like In-sook, certainly not like Kang-jin, not even close. In school and at home where only scholastic excellence counted, I was barely average. This worry gnawed at me.

Dostoyevsky, Tolstoy, Stendhal, even Kafka and Camus, I heard these names thrown about by Mi-hae's university friends when they came to visit, which to me, meant these authors were important. So I tackled them, without a clue what I was reading. Their dense texts and sparse dialogue were over my head. I often found myself waking up from a stupor, my face stuck to the open book, wet from sweat and drooling. Still I kept at it, eventually finding a way to understand them—by approaching them like manhwa.

Even before I could read, I read manhwa, Korean graphic novels. When I say, *read*, I mean *looked*. I looked at the cartoon drawings—the characters' expressions, their action, and changing settings—to decipher the story; the words were almost unnecessary.

With these great books, I learned to filter out their detailed and lengthy descriptions—of vegetation, cloud clusters, the shapes and movements of shadows, their religious, political and philosophical discourses—sticking close to the storylines: what the characters did and said to one another, how their words affected others and reacted, and what the final consequences of their actions were. In the end, working out my own interpretation, and although it may only be partially true, it put ideas into my head.

One such book was *Sarang (Love)* by the master Korean author, Lee Kwang-Soo, a thick, beast of a book. I wanted to know what love was, what it meant, what it did to people. In *Sarang,* a young female teacher falls in love with a brilliant doctor who has an ailing wife. To be close to the doctor, the teacher becomes his nurse, following him from place to place, helping cure people, even taking care of his children and ailing wife. Witnessing their deep love and feeling gratitude, the doctor's wife offers them her dying gift—that they marry. But they never do. Instead, for the rest of their lives, they circle around each other, watching each other make wrong choices and suffer. They love and care for everyone around them, but the love for each other goes unconsummated; all because their love had to be spiritual, transcending obsessive, physical love.

That was a very disappointing end. It felt wrong: a woman and a man striving for the kind of love Jesus had for humanity. If I had to love everyone I knew equally, there'd be nothing left of me: I could never love Yumi or even Lee as I loved Mom. I certainly had no love for Kang-jin or Mi-hae. I stood for exclusive love. And yet, the idea of transcendent love between a man and a woman fascinated me: an all-consuming love that melded physical, emotional and spiritual— the kind of love that inspired you to be better than you had been and be worthy of receiving such love. To be sure, I didn't know what was really involved in physical love, except what I saw in the movie posters, like *Gone With The Wind*, that covered the lighting poles, sidewalk walls, and construction facades.

By the time I got to the library, it was closed for the snow storm emergency. And the unexpected first snow didn't bring good tidings at home either. The shoji door to Kang-jin's room was wide open, bundled books stacked outside, snow covering the tops. Inside, In-sook was crying, wrapping up things. A small pack of pots, bowls, utensils, and a frying pan leaned against the kitchen door. In the main room, Aunt was sorting through the stuff from the chest, and in her shop, gone were the mannequins, one of the sewing machines, the floor fan, and most of the rolled fabric.

Snow or no snow, we were being evicted.

"How will Mom find me?" I thought.

Chapter Fifteen

The freezing morning wind zapped my face. The dirt ground was frozen solid and very slippery underfoot. After we were evicted we remained in Mapo District, but farther out now, in a shack at the western edge of Seoul, closer to the Han River. Situated at the back of Mapo train station, our long downhill street was not suitable for heavy traffic. It was too old and narrow for the daily assault of vehicles of all sizes. Stores selling knick-knacks, coal, hardware, shoe repairs, and so on, occupied either side of our shack and across the street, including a brothel right next door. If this brothel bothered the pious side of Aunt, she never showed it. No one at home ever talked about its existence, no matter how rowdy they got at night.

Our single-room shack was divided into three parts, thanks to Aunt's ingenuity. Her shop, now renamed 'Alteration Shop', was on the far right. It was quite small, about one-third the size of her old one; still it had a display window, a work table, and a long narrow mirror. Her sewing machine and a dummy torso were pushed right up against the window, giving the shop a quick identity. She hung fabrics all around, less to display than to hide the unfinished walls and our living space next to it. The middle space was the smallest: if the four of us women stood in it, we'd be back to belly. But we managed to put all of our kitchen needs there: a tall water urn, a small cupboard for our bowls and pots, a hole in the ground for coal briquettes for cooking and heating the room on the left and the ever-present urine bucket. This middle space served as our kitchen, washroom, toilet and entrance. It had three doors, a fabric door to Aunt's shop on the right, a sliding plastic door to the street in front, and one sliding shoji door to the room left. The room on the left, our main room, had a small window that faced the street. It was large enough to stick your head out, but you wouldn't do that as you just might collide with a pedestrian walking by. With great difficulty we fitted our large chest into it, then everything we owned went into the chest—blankets, pillows, clothes, Uncle's medicine chest, and all so the room would be clear during the day for eating and studying.

Each morning I carried the urine bucket out and expertly dumped the previous night's waste into the street gutter in front of our shack. It was filled to the brim and whenever a truck or bus rumbled by outside the door, the murky surface rippled like a pond in a storm, spilling out on the dirt ground, its yellow tint shimmering in the light, giving off the pungent smell of human waste as it soaked into the dank earth. The bucket stood in the corner by the shack entrance where the four of us peed into it during the night. Going to the outhouse at night was out of the question. No one wanted to walk out into the icy street, pass Aunt's shop door and three other shops, round the corner into the landlord's yard, whose gate, thankfully, was always left unlocked. Once inside the landlord's yard, you went around the water pump, through a narrow dead-end pathway. At the end of the pathway was the outhouse, with the street on one side and a chicken coop on the other; the outhouse didn't have a light. Once you were in the outhouse, the only thing that separated you from passers by was thin strips of uneven wooden board. Any curious pedestrian could easily peek in to see what you were doing.

As I emptied the bucket a bus roared by inches from my face. I always jumped back, never getting used to it. I imagined that one day, a bus might just topple over sideways, and crush me and the shack. Before going back inside, I gave a swift look at our shack, amazed that it remained standing. Defying gravity, it tilted sharply downhill, enduring thunderous vibrations from the incessant traffic, those vibrations I felt in my bones.

When Uncle came home to visit, the five of us slept quite snug, lying side by side, neatly lined up like corpses. Although Kang-jin rarely stayed overnight, when he did, I laid at everyone's feet against the door since I was the smallest, where I was occasionally kicked by rough sleepers. I'd forgotten to grow since Mom left. I was once one of the tallest of my classmates, but now, I found myself standing in the front row everywhere. One good thing about the loss of privacy: I was safe from Kang-jin.

● ● ●

The new year 1972 was just a few days ahead. It already boded well for me, as Aunt promised me a new coat, one of her old coats. I'd finally leave the one I was wearing, which was In-sook's before and originally it was Mi-hae's. With Aunt's mantra being, *good clothing gives you wings, it opens doors for you,* she took excellent care of clothes and wore them well.

All students wore mandatory uniforms, reflecting the government's effort to equalize the visual difference between the wealthy and the poor. But it didn't work: we all knew who was who. Nothing escaped our fourteen-year-old girls' eyes: the well-tailored coat; the thick, long scarf that wrapped around the neck many times over; the daily sparkling white collar and handkerchief; scratch-free schoolbag; the multiple-layered lunch box containing sumptuous food—all signs of wealth. Observing these details, we put each other into categories.

"The coat you want, yes, the one with the fur collar is at the bottom of the second drawer," Aunt said. Bring that out for me, it will need taking in." The coat she was giving me was made of soft, thick black wool. For school, it had to be either navy or black. Aunt would remove the fur collar when she altered it to my size. She kept most of her clothes in the second from the bottom drawer of the chest, neatly folded, although shabby from years of wear and tear. But when I opened the drawer, the smell inside made me choke; the same smell I'd been smelling for days, and a different kind of stench than I was used to. I just couldn't pinpoint from where it came. I had been telling the others about it, but they didn't smell a thing. Aunt said my nose was imagining things again.

The smell got stronger as I lifted the top layer of clothes. A stinging, make-you-gasp kind of odour hit my nose. And there, at the bottom of the drawer, nestled in Aunt's old coat, a half dozen or more wet newborn rats were suckling at their mom's teats; their tiny bodies lying limp like uncooked finger sausages—greyish, pinkish tiny monsters. Littered around them were chewed up fur bits, black shiny droppings, slimy birthing matter, and dark blood stains, all matted on Aunt's fur collar and the lining of the coat.

The most horrible sight was the tiny white bones strewn around the mom rat, evidence that she ate her own. Sparkling against the room's light bulb, the mom rat's beady eyes stared at me, emotionless and passive.

She didn't look scared, didn't move at all; this was her cosy home and me, the intruder. I fell back.

Everyone rushed over to look.

Aunt said to Uncle, "Honey, take them out."

"With a wash and an alteration, it'll be as good as new," Aunt said to me.

I knew I wouldn't wear it. I wore In-sook's old coat again.

Chapter Sixteen

It was March 1972.

This March morning felt more ferocious than any February morning, perhaps because my thoughts were already anticipating the coming spring. February was and is my favourite month; from its darkest, coldest days, when winter is at its harshest, there are signs of life quietly emerging, pushing upwards for the sun and open air—the old can't overcome the young, winter must yield to the spring.

The March sun was slow to rise so it was still dark and icy cold. Every morning I made two trips to the landlord's yard to fill up our water urn, so Aunt could cook rice and others wash; we took turns washing for lack of space. The freezing water pump handle burned my palm, ready to take off my skin.

From the dark street, I could see In-sook ending an all night study session in Aunt's shop, a dim light above her head and work books. Like a single-minded homing pigeon, she lived for one thing—to get into Seoul National University. If she succeeded, we'd have two Seoul National University graduates, an incredible achievement for any family. Aunt's status would sky-rocket, giving her a well-deserved bragging right, making up for all the suffering and poverty she'd had to endure. But first In-sook would have to pass the high school entrance exam, then three more years of gruelling high school.

Studying in a dim light night after night, In-sook became near sighted, hampering her studies. Somehow, Aunt got her a pair of glasses which were very expensive for us. Eye glasses were thought to be too bookish, a blemish on a young woman, but In-sook wore them proudly. I liked them on her too; she looked smart and they hid her many facial shortcomings. Only 15 years old, In-sook already had pimples dotting her coarse forehead and cheeks, angry red and white blemishes. They threatened to burst and when they did, they took bits of her flesh with them, leaving permanent marks. The straight nose, so perfect on Kang-jin and Mi-hae, grew just a bit too long and wide on In-sook, but she didn't care.

In-sook and Aunt were not alone in this quest for all-consuming scholastic achievement; every parent and student were whipped up in it. A usual sight at school at the end of each day was moms and house-keepers crowding the school gate, waiting to hand over hot meals, so their kids could eat on the run. After school, students went directly to private tutors or night academies till curfew, only to start all over again at 6.00 a.m. for the morning academy before school started. In-sook went to the night academy, although Aunt didn't wait at the school gate with a meal. That much luxury, she didn't have.

I didn't go to night academy; Aunt could barely afford to send In-sook there. Aunt never looked over my shoulder to see if I studied, nor asked for my report cards, nor scolded me for coming home late or disappearing all day on weekends. I was free to do whatever I wanted and go wherever I chose. My friends also went to night academies so I spent most of my off-school hours in the library or at the churches listening to music. But as the years passed, this freedom became unnerving. I felt lost at school and at home, abandoned, being pushed off to the fringe of things. Deep inside, I was terrified of not getting into a decent high school; I was failing almost every subject except music and art, two subjects that were useless for getting into a good school. I had heard of a special school dedicated to musically talented kids. Imagine, studying music and singing all day long; it shouldn't even be called a school. But no one around me knew about such a school or where it was, how you were chosen, what it cost. It wasn't as if I could simply make a telephone call and ask for details of this special school. I'd never even been in a telephone booth but they were just beginning to pop up in our area. If I ever mentioned such a school to Aunt, she'd look at me as if I had gone off my head. When the panic about my future became unbearable, I thought about Mom and studying in America. It comforted me.

• • •

The classroom felt unnervingly quiet, with excited rustling of papers the only noise. Some already seemed to know something unusual had happened or was about to happen. Everyone hushed when Miss Go came in for roll call, and the reason for our excitement followed in behind her; a new transfer student. But she was no ordinary new student; although she looked like us, she was not one of us. Her soft, round, cherub-like face was well shaped by her abundant head of hair, cut at the ear like ours, but somewhat looser, a bit unkempt without looking untidy. Her eyes didn't have our sharp alertness, our battle-ready, competitive look. Her uniform fit was loose and awkward, although there was nothing really to fault. Even before she opened her mouth, we just knew she was a foreigner.

Like Mom, many people had left South Korea after the war, seeking a better life in far away countries, America being the most coveted place. People rarely came back so a family returning to Korea was rare. Miss Go told us why this student had returned: her father was a Korean diplomat who had been stationed in America for years and had now been called back home.

When Miss Go told her to say hello and introduce herself to the class, we were spellbound: she spoke in halting, unsure Korean. Her name was Hae-ra. Her soft American accent sounded as if she had a mouthful of cotton candy and gave her an innocent and vulnerable air. She looked at us like a child would—openly, vaguely trusting. You wanted to run over to her, pat her and say, there, there. This difference made her immediately and immensely attractive, glowing like a brilliant sunflower in a field of daisies. We gaped, mesmerised; we fell instantly in love.

Later in our English class, Miss Go told Hae-ra to read a passage from our textbook. Her reading came to us like music: melodic, fluid, lovely—what contrast. We struggled greatly with 'th' and 'v' sounds. We mispronounced 'l' and 'r'; our tongues unable to differentiate. Our reading of the English textbook was halting, less fluent.

Listening to her reading, I thought of the green-eyed man, of his carefree body language, his open gaze, and his efforts to speak Korean with a similar muffled accent, utterly charming like Hae-ra. But my thoughts hurt; I didn't want to go there—to be reminded of Mom, whose face had become fuzzy over the years, almost mythical, something I held on to only at night. The less I made her real, the easier my daily life, except when I was terrified about my future.

I wanted to ignore this new student, but all I could do was stare at her.

Today was a day full of surprises. Miss Go ended our English class early, saying she had one more announcement. She began by praising our class president, Doo-sun, for her initiative and then the entire class for their community spirit, compassion and love for our fellow classmates, taking care of each other in time of need.

Doo-sun walked up to the front of the classroom, holding a thick envelope. She thanked everyone for coming together in this effort, and said she was proud to present this emergency fund to the classmate who most deserved our concern and care.

Sook-ja, who sat not far from me, had her head down as usual, her fingers fidgeting with her hair, looking as if she wasn't listening, but she had to be listening: how well this fund would help with her mom's medication, put food on the table, and afford her lunch.

Doo-sun had finished her speech. Silence. Sook-ja didn't get up. Actually Doo-sun didn't mention her name. Then Yumi jabbed me with her elbow; all eyes were on me, smiling. It was for me that they collected the fund. I looked down, not knowing what to do. I felt hot all over. No wonder I didn't know about the fund; no one asked me to contribute.

Yumi nudged me again, this time indicating that I should go to the front and accept the fund. I got up but couldn't move, my feet melting like wax. I hung on to the edge of my desk. Doo-sun went on to say that I was a wonderful singer and painter. This fund was to help me get through the term. Then with a wink in her voice, she said they were counting on me to win our city-wide choir competition and hopefully another medal for the class at the school's painting competition, like I did last year. Her speech felt like an eternity, yet it was over too quickly. I squirmed, ashamed to stand up full height. The room was quiet, everyone waiting for me to come up and accept the envelope, and perhaps even give a thank you speech. I didn't. I couldn't. I leaned on my desk for support. I mumbled, doing my best to calm the shaking: "There must be some mistake. I don't need financial help. I'm fine. Please give it to someone who needs it." I sat down, whisperings all around. My seat felt like it was made of nails. I got hotter and hotter every passing second. I wanted to evaporate.

Miss Go quietly said, "Yes, there must have been a mistake." She then told Doo-sun to put the envelope away till they figured out what to do with it.

The lunch bell rang. Yumi nudged me: "Let's eat!" The classroom buzzed and students opened their bento boxes. Some got up and stretched but I walked out. I ran an entire street, trying to shake loose the shame that clung to me. I didn't want them to look at me that way—smiles mixed with pity, all the while thinking, poor, poor Su-young. I didn't want pity. The humiliation lit up again, eating at me. I ran faster. And of all the days, why did it have to be today? When the new transfer student would forever remember me by it.

I didn't know my poverty was that obvious. I didn't know I was worse off even than Sook-ja. Then the hate raged in me. I hated myself for feeling conflicted. Part of me regretted not accepting the fund because that money would really have helped. I could pay the tuition that was due last December. Could I go back and accept it? I could share it with Sook-ja; that would make me feel better, less shamed. I shook off that thought. Sook-ja was just an excuse. I stomped my feet. Where was my pride?

I wandered about the streets going over and over the classroom scene, unable to shake off the discomfort and anger. I promised myself that when I got home I would ask Aunt for my tuition, no matter what. I'd beg, cry, and get punished, if need be. Then it dawned on me: I had never heard In-sook or Mi-hae complaining about their tuition fees being delayed. I had never heard In-sook badgering Aunt about her books or school materials.

When I got home, an unusually lavish dinner waited: spinach and clam soup, grilled mackerel and full bowls of rice. It's been a long time since we ate this well. After dinner, Aunt wanted a stroll—our first after-dinner stroll since moving here. Was this a good omen? At least it was a right setting to ask for my tuition fees to be paid.

Aunt walked, looking relaxed, delighting in fresh air, In-sook and I trailing behind her. We walked up the steep hill all the way to the train station. The plaza was thinning out, people rushing to make their last trains. Vendors at the edges of the plaza were striking their tents for the day.

Aunt stopped at the vendor who made sticky buns filled with brown sugar. She bought each of us one, a wonderful treat for a chilly night. Then we turned around homebound. I still hadn't asked for the tuition money, afraid of ruining this perfect evening. I'd already decided not to tell Aunt about the poverty fund my classmates offered. It would humiliate her as it did me. Or worse, she might get angry and say I was a fool not to take it.

Finally I let it out, cautiously: "Aunt, my tuition, could we pay just part of it, so it would ease things a bit at school? Miss Go said if I don't bring the tuition soon, you'll have to come to school to explain, or she'll make a house visit."

Aunt walked on as if she didn't hear me. But after a quiet few steps, she said, "You'll have your tuition tomorrow." Her face was serene, inscrutable. So I kept mine serene too, although the doubt bubbled up. Did I really hear that? What if she changes her mind?

The rest of the walk home was enchanting. The cold air cooled our hot fingers, sticky from the molten flow of sweetness leaking from the buns. Out of the blue, Aunt held my hand and In-sook's; we walked on holding hands. Her thin dry hand felt good, familiar even, although I couldn't recall ever holding her hand before. The midnight curfew siren wouldn't sound for another hour or so, but the buses and taxis were already scurrying away with their last passengers. Below us, the city had already gone to sleep, the dark sky making us feel as though we were walking into the star-filled heavens. My heart swelled, an inexplicable happiness sweeping over me. In-sook must have felt the same. She bolted out in front of us, and opening her arms wide, she circled and glided like a graceful dragonfly in flight. I held on tight to Aunt's hand. I imagined a benevolent Aunt, a loving Aunt. I pretended I was one of her children. For this night, I felt I belonged to her, I wanted to belong to her, urgently. I wanted her to love me like she loved In-sook, so I'd feel safe like In-sook. And instead of crying to sleep, I'd dream, curled up against her, and from that strength, I could go on, to study hard and to look forward to my life ahead.

For this night, all was well.

Chapter Seventeen

Like a stalker, I peeped in through the small square window of Miss Jung's room, watching and listening: her gaunt figure was bent over like a stork. She was playing a passage from one of Schubert's Impromptus; fluid, joyful, like a conversation between lovers. I knew the music although I couldn't spell or pronounce its name correctly. I'd heard Miss Jung play in the past, and I'd heard Schubert's music on her record player performed by a Russian pianist, the most revered, she'd said. I watched her in fascination. No matter how fast her fingers flew, her body stayed still, for she was an understated person; she never exaggerated, in words or in action.

One day in the middle of our term, Miss Jung appeared and took over our choir as a visiting music teacher. We heard she was our alumnus and a Catholic nun. She didn't wear a nun's habit to school, but a long-sleeved black sweater over a white blouse and a black skirt, and wore thick round glasses on her rather beaky nose. She didn't have her own class of students, or a desk in the teachers' hall. Instead, her room was attached at the back of the auditorium, secluded from the main part of the school. She didn't act like our other formidable teachers, nor mingle with them, and she never used her ruler to discipline us. She was a mystery to all of us: always alone, belonging to no one, beholden to no one. She knew each of us from her class only. Even when we got to know each other well, she never asked personal or school life questions, although I suspected she already knew of my difficulties. My poverty was self-evident. She was the coolest person I knew.

Quite early on, she picked me out during our chorus rehearsal and asked me to sing a phrase from the music we were working on. She didn't say anything then and we carried on. Not long after, she told me to come to her office after school; she asked me to sing again. Then she assigned me a solo part and said, if I wanted, I could visit her and she would teach me how to improve my singing. So whenever I could—during lunch time or after school—I pestered her. She didn't mind, almost always inviting me in. But sometimes I didn't let her know I was at the door, especially when she was playing the piano. Like Mom used to do when I had my piano lessons, I listened and watched her through the window, so I wouldn't disturb her concentration.

With her mentoring, I found a purpose and a reason to come to school. Besides a few string and wind instruments and the upright piano in the room, Miss Jung had a record player on her desk. From this machine, I heard music I had never heard before, the Gregorian Chant, for one. Our traditional Korean vocal music, Pansori, was sung by one singer who theatrically impersonated all the characters in the story, including the sound effects; the rain falling, someone laughing, or the fury of swishing winds; it was rich, colourful, dramatic. But the Gregorian Chant was exactly the opposite: mysterious and soothing, male voices in unison meandered in a foggy mist; pliant, undulating, without earthly desires, putting you in a state of being in another world. She introduced me to Bach, Vivaldi, Beethoven and others, patiently explaining their music and lives. On one occasion she played a recording of Handel's *Dixit Dominus*. Its beauty made my heart soar; everything else fell away while two sopranos sang, their voices weaving in and around each other, all the while rising higher and higher; I could hardly breathe, suspended in their ethereal sounds. God surely had to be in their voices.

Miss Jung took a keen interest in our city wide chorus competition. She wanted us to win. We had three pieces to prepare for the competition. She chose the final piece with me starting as a soloist, and so our unofficial, somewhat clandestine voice lessons began, sometimes even on Saturdays. Besides scales, she taught me Italian art songs, for their pure lines, to give the voice a *bel canto* foundation, she said. She told me to think of the entire song as a single thought, a single breath, to give the legato lines the smooth flow, even for the fast passages, even through the piano intro, interlude, and all the way to the end. She opened up my upper range, going above high C with fast scale exercises. During these exercises, she made me stand back, away from the piano keyboard, so I wouldn't get self-conscious about how high I was singing, but I already knew, because I remembered the notes of the piano.

As she predicted, our chorus passed through the regional level. We were one of four finalists. Our nerves and excitement ran high for the final round.

• • •

We filed into the packed auditorium with teachers, parents and students from all over Seoul. We stood in compact rows of three. Miss Jung placed me in the front row of the soprano section, slightly to her left.

She slowly lifted her arms out, holding us with her gaze, then opened her palms ever so gently, like letting a baby bird free. With that single motion, we became one, our four-part harmony sounding as if from a single person. Mozart's *Ave Verum Corpus* was the required first selection; a quiet and celestial piece. Next came a Korean bird song, a well-known folk song rearranged for the chorus. It didn't naturally lend itself to harmonizing, but Miss Jung used our voices effectively by having some of us mimic the chirping of birds, others imitating the joyful sounds farmers made during the harvest; the audience went wild, some joining in, waving and dipping their arms—the familiar dancing arms every Korean did when happy. They gave us a thunderous applause despite our having one more piece to perform.

Miss Jung waited for us and the audience to settle down. At last she looked at me, then closed her eyes: a signal that I sing the first verse of *Panis Angelicus* by Cesar Frank that we had rehearsed so many times. All choruses sang a cappella. The only instrument allowed was a tiny pitch pipe that at the beginning of each piece, someone discreetly blew to give the starting note. But with this last piece, Miss Jung forbade the pitch pipe, saying it would be far more effective and impressive if I sang without any aid, and then from my lead, the chorus would join in. But the unexpected applause and excitement in the room threw me off. I wasn't sure if I could find the exact pitch or sing in tune all the way through. Uncomfortable silence filled the room. Then as if she had read my mind, Miss Jung looked up at me and gave the most radiant smile that we had ever seen from her. With that, I relaxed into the explosive "pa," and sang. Then Miss Jung signalled our chorus to join in; their four-part harmony enfolding and lifting me. Soon our voices soared to the ceiling, to the far end of the auditorium, then returning back to us; even we were in awe at such sublime beauty, ringing and pulsating long after our sound had died down. The auditorium went dead quiet, followed by the applause that shook the room. We brought our school the first place medal.

A week after the competition, Miss Jung's room went dark. Her half-year term was finished. Her next stop was Vietnam, into the thick of the Vietnam war, to help and comfort Korean soldiers fighting alongside Americans.

Her last words to me were that I should continue my singing and that if I wished, I could write to her and send the letters to her convent, she'd receive them wherever she might be.

Chapter Eighteen

"Look at it. No, no, not the face, that's a pancake. You should've seen her mom though; a heartbreaker face . . . melt you in seconds. Cute? Her? Really? You've gone bat blind. But, she's got something special . . . *look* at those boobs."

"Oh, yeah."

"Yeah, I see what you mean."

"Those ought to tell you what she's good for."

"They seem bigger because she's small."

"How old is she?"

"She's in middle school. How old are you now?" Kang-jin asked. I didn't answer.

"Wow, they're like melons!"

"First rate beauties, aren't they?"

"Luscious."

"Have you had some already?"

"Hahahaha. . . ."

They were staring at my chest. Their furtive polite whispers in the beginning had shifted to a free-for-all commenting and chortling. One man pointed his finger at my chest, said something to the man next; he nodded vigorously in agreement; others wanted to know what they were talking about. They were told then they all convulsed with barking laughter.

Home from school, I'd walked into a room full of drunken men. Kang-jin said I should stay, wanted to introduce me to his friends. There was a threat in his voice, so I stayed put. Six men, in their military buzz cuts, sat cross-legged around the low table, Kang-jin in the middle.

They toasted with another round of soju, the Korean vodka. I kept my head down, pulling my sock over the big toe that stuck out from the hole.

"Now friends, do I have a treat for you! She can sing anything!" Kang-jin offered magnanimously, his face flushed from drinking. Six red faces leered at me.

"Sing Arirang!"someone shouted, hitting the table.

Everyone nodded, ogling, expectant.

"Su-young-ah, sing something. Anything. Let's have some fun!" Kang-jin cajoled.

They began clapping and tapping the table. Empty soju bottles rattled, some rolled, clanging against each other. A dozen or so unopened soju bottles threatened to topple over. The room smelled of alcohol, cigarettes, roasted squid legs and sweat.

"Come on. Su-young-aaaah. Sing!" Kang-jin's slurring voice insisted.

The pounding got louder, soon in unison.

"l wanna see if her singing matches her melons. Sing big," someone bellowed.

"Watch her nose when she sings. Her nostrils flare in and out, in and out. The funniest thing . . ."

How did he know what my nose did when l sang? Then l remembered: at church when l sang solos.

"If you don't wanna sing, show us your tits," another shouted.

One of them lunged at me. He fell face first, his forehead thudding on the floor.

"Whahahaha!"

Some fell sideways, overcome with laughing fits. l felt wetness on my legs. l looked down; l had peed, was peeing still, down to my socks, spreading out to the floor. Before l could run, the fallen man clutched my leg and looked up my skirt. He rubbed his hand up and down my wet leg, then put his fingers up to his nose, smelling them, then licking them. Everyone howled, completely losing it. l shot out of the room, ran to the landlord's house, to the pathway between the outhouse and chicken coop. l sat on the rotting straw, chicken poop and feed. The chickens didn't care, pecking away at the feed around me. l was shivering. l needed to change my clothes. l wanted to tear them off. l wanted to scream, l wanted to punish something, anything; the shame wanted revenge, but there was nothing around me, so l hit myself. l hit my head, chest, pinched my arms and legs as hard as l could. l wished for a bus to fall on our shack.

"What's wrong with singing a little for Kang-jin and his friends? How often does he come home? What's so precious about your singing? Does it bring us money? When did you get all so uppity?" Aunt later scolded me for making a fuss over nothing, when all he wanted was to show off his little sister's singing.

The men were his army buddies come to celebrate the end of his mandatory military service. This three-year sacrifice cut into most young men's education, but no one escaped it. Now Kang-jin would go back to his tutoring home and finish his university.

But after only three days he rushed back to our shack because a major scandal broke out at home.

"Did I ever ask you to do that for me? How could you! How is it even possible? What if my friends, what if the school found out? They could take my scholarship away!" Kang-jin was screaming like a mad man, pacing the room, looming over at Aunt and Uncle. In-sook and I, who knew nothing of what happened, stood, huddled in the corner, dying to find out what this was all about. We'd seen Kang-jin and Uncle fight before, many times, but never like this.

"You are the elders of the church, for God's sake! The humiliation of it all, I'd rather kill myself!" Kang-jin punched the shoji door frame. The room shook.

"Let's talk calmly. Kang-jin-ah, please. Sit, sit down," Mi-hae pleaded.

"Was any of it real, you being Christians? You've ruined me, us! I'm so sick of all—all this, you, this stinking family!" So incensed, Kang-jin grabbed the water bowl, threw it. The bowl hit the wall, water splashed over Uncle's pants and the floor.

Uncle, who never made a sudden move, rose up with an incredible agility, lunged at Kang-jin and grabbed his shoulders; Aunt and Mi-hae got between them, trying to separate them. In-sook crouched in the corner, curled up in a ball, crying.

"You ungrateful bastard. Yes, let's end it right here, right now. Why go on living? We've wasted our lives. All that hard work and suffering, just to raise an arrogant shit for a son!" Uncle shouted, "Yeah, you're the great Seoul University man! You think you did that all by yourself. What about our sacrifice? Now all we've got is a selfish, thankless bastard for a son. What's the point. Let's just all die together!"

Shoving Aunt and Mi-hae aside, Uncle hurled himself at Kang-jin, going after his throat. Kang-jin fell backward. They flew into the kitchen, shattering the door. The urine bucket clanged and somersaulted. Uncle punched Kang-jin in the jaw; Kang-jin, the stronger one, got on top and gripped Uncle's throat, choking him; Uncle worked to fend him off. Aunt, normally a defender of Kang-jin, began bashing his head with the urine bucket, screaming for him to stop. Kang-jin let go and got up, looking stunned at his action. Uncle got up too. Then he walked over to the cupboard and took out the kitchen knife and came at Kang-jin. With one last frustrated howl, Kang-jin ran out of the shack.

"You're not my son any more, you fucking bastard! Don't you ever come back! I swear I will kill you," Uncle bellowed after him.

In-sook and I didn't dare ask what this was all about. But the next day, Sunday, at the church, I found out.

For the first time ever, Aunt and Uncle didn't go to church that day. I had a solo to sing, so I went. But as soon as I arrived at church, I felt something was wrong. Chorus members avoided me. It was highly unusual as they were kind and treated me well for my singing, and also because I was the niece of the founding member of the church. Today, the congregation was only half the size. The worship room felt unsettled too; instead of quiet prayers before the service, parishioners were clustered together, talking, shaking their heads. There was no sign of elders or Pastor Lim.

At last, an elder came in and announced that there wouldn't be a church service that day. Instead, they were holding an emergency elders' meeting.

I went to the backroom to hang up my choir robe and from the meeting room next door, I heard someone say, "Elder Kim," Aunt's title. I hung by the door and listened.

Sorting from their angry shouts and blames, I put together three stunning facts.

First, Aunt and Uncle were charged with embezzling the new building fund that the church had been raising for years, almost from the beginning. Second, Pastor Lim was being fired for being careless; he and

Aunt were responsible for overseeing the fund. Third, the reason for Pastor Lim's carelessness, or as one of the elders put it, "Looking the other way", was because he and Aunt were having an affair. The church keeper saw them, he swore.

I couldn't help bursting out laughing. It was absurd, Aunt and Pastor Lim as lovers. It was physically impossible. Pastor Lim was truly old. His face reminded me of a Chinese Shar-Pei dog, the folds from his chin cascading to his neck, wagging wildly against his white collar, hypnotising me during his sermons. Leaning on his cane, he walked with some effort. But then I remembered he did come to our old home often, for special prayer sessions or to discuss church matters. We kids always scurried out, giving them privacy. Even when we moved to our current crumbling shack, he visited us. And now, looking back, his visits took on a different meaning and shade. Still, I had a hard time believing that part of the accusation.

Within a couple of weeks, everything came to light. Aunt indeed used the church fund for our education and to put food on the table. Uncle had little to do with the embezzlement, for one obvious reason: he was rarely home. But the church elders leniently agreed that Uncle could take the blame, so Aunt could remain home to take care of the family. He received a two-year jail sentence.

But Uncle came home in six months, a changed man. We almost didn't recognise him. His handsome face no longer bore the kindness that made him so attractive. He now wore a blank mask, expressing nothing. He never spoke again; it was as if he was mute all his life. He didn't seem to know any of us. We sensed he heard us, but he didn't respond with words. He ate but little. He never read again, not his medical books, not even his beloved newspaper *Hankook Iibo*. He sat and looked out of our tiny window facing the street. Nothing rattled him, not even an occasional huge truck that roared deafeningly. And he slept. He never went outside again except to go to the outhouse; Aunt accompanied him then. It was unnerving to us all. Eventually he became a piece of furniture to us, like the tall chest behind him. And after a while, we stopped noticing him. Uncle never went back up north. Aunt found another church to join, far away from the old one.

Chapter Nineteen

Aunt turned our shack upside down in her manic effort to make it presentable. All morning, I'd been following her orders, mending and cleaning. Even In-sook and Mi-hae took a break from their studies to help. Today, Kang-jin was bringing his fiancée home.

Despite their violent fight, Kang-jin stood by Uncle all through the trial and his prison term. Whatever Kang-jin felt in private, he never showed his shame of being a convict's son. He visited the prison regularly. When Uncle got sick in the prison, it was Kang-jin who fought to get him discharged, successfully cutting Uncle's two-year sentence to six months.

No one had met Kang-jin's fiancée except Mi-hae. We knew only a few things about her. Her name was Jae-in and she and Kang-jin both went to Seoul University, which was jaw-droppingly impressive, although Aunt worried that she might be too brainy for a daughter-in-law. They had been dating for five years, even through Kang-jin's three-year mandatory military service—many young couples didn't survive those years of separation. Kang-jin had been tutoring her two nephews for years and that was how they met. Most shockingly, she was the only daughter of a family who owned a large hospital in Seoul where her father was the chief heart surgeon, and she would join his practice as soon as she finished her medical training.

We were told that initially, her family didn't approve of their relationship; the wealthy didn't mingle with the poor. We were poorer than poor. And not just poor, we also lacked connections, having no powerful friends or relatives. But Aunt was undaunted, boasting that Kang-jin was too good for Jae-in: "With his looks and academic excellence, as soon as he finishes his law degree, all of South Korea will line up to take him as a son-in-law!" It was said that once you got into Seoul National University, the whole world lay at your feet.

Aunt had devoted her life to him, and Kang-jin, in turn, took his first son's responsibility seriously. Korean tradition called for the first son to take care of the parents in their old age—not the second son, nor the third, and definitely not daughters: the daughter became the daughter of her in-laws. When Kang-jin married, it was expected that he and his bride would live with Aunt and Uncle, and take care of them till their dying day. Aunt was counting on living in a grand home Kang-jin would provide.

Earlier at breakfast, Aunt prayed fervently and at length, thanking God for making her struggles and hardships not to have been in vain; for hearing her prayers, vindicating her from all those who trampled her down and spat at her; for never taking his eyes from her, his faithful daughter. Today was her reward, and from this day on, only the brightest future shone ahead. Then in a sudden flash of anger, Aunt banged her chopsticks on the table. "If she thinks I'm going to bow down to her just because she comes from money, she'd be oh-so-wrong. I won't have it. I won't have an arrogant bitch for a daughter-in-law. No, it won't happen! And mark my words, her family will try to humiliate me, showing off their wealth, doling out pennies like we're a charity case. I won't kowtow to them; I'd sooner kill myself! I come from money too, far richer than they are. We owned half of the mining in North Korea! I know wealth, been there. I bet they are new money, and God only knows what they did to get it. No one gets rich keeping themselves clean. And who's ever heard of that last name, Yang. Probably their ancestors are not even Koreans, but Chinese."

We had heard, many times, of our Grandparents' mining company, but every time Aunt talked about it, it grew in size and grandeur.

"And why couldn't we meet her in a restaurant? Why does he have to bring her into this shit-hole? He's still mad at me, that's what, wants to humiliate me, showing off his rich girlfriend, punishing me for his father going to jail . . ." She stopped short, checking herself. We never, ever talked about Uncle having been in jail. It was as if he had gone up north for a while and came home sick and never went back.

"Mom, he just wants to introduce her to all of us, including father. You know he can't go to a restaurant," In-sook soothed her.

"Well, I guess she'll have to know how we live sooner or later," Aunt said, "I just hope she won't change her mind and break it off. Really . . . who would want to marry into this poor family? Ugh. Money is the enemy . . . money, not people,"

Using my fingers and palm, I kept pressing on the frayed edges of wallpaper that was once white. But no matter how much glue I added, the edges fell away, brittle from ageing and the stress of repeatedly getting wet from the leaky ceiling. It could've been the glue's fault. I made it by squashing leftover rice, adding a little water to make it liquid, like Uncle used to. There was not much more I could do here so I brought out the cushions and placed them strategically on the bald and damaged spots on the floor. These cushions came out only for important occasions; the last time was when Kang-jin's army buddies visited.

Uncle was sleeping, facing the wall. Aunt would have to get him up and make him look decent for the visitor.

My next task was to cover the kitchen area with fresh soil. From time to time the ground got too wet and stinky, odours accumulated from the overflowing urine and from the splattering when we washed and cooked. I brought some soil from the alleyway, removed the old and added the new, patting it down, making the stench disappear for the time being.

"Careful! Don't you get me dirty. I've just put on a clean dress," Mi-hae said, cutting up apples by the cupboard.

Aunt was thoroughly spent, vacillating between excitement and agitation. Although she didn't normally sweat, she was wiping her armpits when Kang-jin opened the door. Jae-in, the fiancée, walked in.

Aunt quickly found her composure. "Why on earth would such a beautiful, precious young lady want to be part of this dirt-poor family?" was her opening greeting.

Jae-in simply gave a deep bow.

Aunt went inside our main room first and took the honoured place, opposite the door. Before they sat, Jae-in and Kang-jin bowed to Aunt, this time properly, bending from their waists, heads touching the floor. Given how wealthy she was and how poor we were, we felt quite awkward at this display. Aunt didn't flinch. Thus the ritual began: the meeting with the in-laws.

Jae-in demurely took off her thick black coat. Under it, she wore a simple puff sleeved sweater and a long grey skirt that modestly covered her legs; it was considered bad manners to show legs to a future mother-in-law. The only sign of her wealth was a gold watch on her slender wrist. Her blemish-free face was soap-clean and pale. She overpowered everyone in the room with her height, taller even than Kang-jin, but the most striking thing about her was her stillness. Once she sat, she didn't move. It gave her an aura of dignity, elegance, even royalty—although I never met anyone royal. She spoke beautifully, addressing Aunt in a polite form, every sentence complete, measured, and thoughtful. Then Jae-in flinched, stopping her eloquent greeting speech midway as a bus thundered by outside. We'd become so used to these roaring noises outside, we no longer paid any attention to them, but now we became acutely aware and prayed that there wouldn't be another until after the meeting. And Jae-in looked uncomfortable sitting on the floor, like she wasn't used to it. We'd heard that some very wealthy homes had adopted the Western style of living, using chairs to sit in their living rooms and stretching out on plush beds dedicated for sleeping like the one I saw on Mom's army base. But I suspected her discomfort came from something else.

Jae-in didn't know what to do in front of her future mother-in-law, especially in this dismal, as Aunt aptly put it, "rat's ass" of a place. The ritual of meeting the Korean mother-in-law was the great terror for all future Korean wives, and all mothers-in-law gleefully looked forward to it. Although the rules slackened after the war, a mother-in-law was still a formidable figure. Aunt could easily stop Kang-jin from marrying a woman she didn't approve of. And Aunt, even in this abysmal setting, matched the hauteur of any mother-in-law to be, sitting tall, her thin frame erect. Like a gambler with her last chips, she put her poverty on the table, daring Jae-in to bow down to her. But like a knife-juggling magician, Kang-jin skilfully balanced his loyalty to Aunt with Jae-in's comfort, feeding Aunt a piece of apple with both his hands, touching Jae-in's arm ever so slightly to reassure her that he was right there with her. Kang-jin introduced his younger sisters to Jae-in, adding me, too, as his sister.

Aunt looked quite satisfied at the meeting's progress, although from time to time she adjusted her blouse, as the extra padding inside her bra kept riding up. Especially for meeting a future family member, she was worried about her looks. Her pride and fighting spirit still in fine form.

Suddenly, we heard a stir, followed by a stink that overwhelmed the room. In the dark corner, Uncle was trying to stand up, his old boxer briefs soiled front and back. He had nothing else on; his concave chest sinking into the flabby folds of his stomach. Huddled in the corner with a sheet over his skeletal body, we had forgotten him. And Aunt, so distracted, forgot to take him to the outhouse. Before any of us could react, he collapsed back, sitting on his soiled briefs, staring at Jae-in with his vacant eyes. Kang-jin and In-sook rushed over and took him out. I brought in wet rags to clean the mess he left.

"He's been that way for over a year now," Aunt said evenly, no apologies.

Jae-in, equally calm, told Aunt that she already knew about his condition, and if Aunt agreed, she'd be honoured to admit Uncle to her family's hospital for a thorough checkup and treatment.

"Oh, wouldn't that be wonderful, finally to find out what's wrong with him. We couldn't afford to take him to a hospital . . ." Aunt let the last sentence hang, then said, "But we don't want to put you out. A hospital visit is very expensive. We couldn't do that to you."

So, Jae-in invited one more time, as was the custom.

"Well, we will think about it. But thank you for the offer," Aunt left it vague. No one accepted a favour when first offered. That would look too impolite. Jae-in didn't pursue it further, that would be deemed too aggressive, showing off. But both knew it was a done deal.

As the tradition required, Jae-in brought gifts—beautifully wrapped, important gifts. A slick, polished wooden box for Uncle; in it, shrouded in golden silk, were three red ginseng roots, as big as my hand, their shape almost human. We had only seen a whole ginseng in Korean traditional pharmacies, floating in an encased glass jar. Even when Uncle was practising his Chinese medicine, he bought regular white ginseng, often already sliced. Then he sliced it even thinner. Red ginseng, which was not really red but more of a light persimmon colour, was very rare and prohibitively expensive. Our jaws dropped when she told us that these ginsengs were over fifty years old.

Jae-in brought Aunt a basketful of fresh fruits, amazingly in this winter, and a box of prime beef. She looked chagrined at a missing gift, for me. She didn't know I existed. I quickly left the room with an excuse to bring more water.

"It's a good thing she isn't too beautiful," Aunt declared after Kang-jin and Jae-in left, stretching her legs out, looking as content as a cat after a good meal. It had been a long while since we'd seen her happy. "A pretty wife is always trouble. How I worry about you, Mi-hae! Who's ever going to take you for a wife with that face of yours," she complained, but she didn't fool any of us. She was proud of Mi-hae's beauty; she predicted her beauty would capture very wealthy in-laws.

I looked forward to Kang-jin getting married too. He would never again come home for an overnight stay.

Chapter Twenty

Soon after Jae-in's visit, her family invited our family to a formal dinner. I wasn't included, but heard their excited talk when they got home. Jae-in's father repeated the invitation to Uncle to be their honoured patient, complete with a private room. Aunt graciously accepted the offer.

Today, everyone went to Jae-in's hospital. Aunt would stay with Uncle through the visit, while Mi-hae and In-sook would go to a dinner given by Jae-in—a lavish dinner was expected. Even though Mi-hae and In-sook were younger than her, Jae-in was required to honour and respect her sisters-in-law as her elders and work to earn their confidence. Mi-hae and In-sook were younger versions of Aunt and could turn powerfully against her.

With everyone away, the shack was all mine. Finally I could look for Mom's letters once more. This time I would succeed; I planned to go through the shack, end to end, even if it took all day. I started with Aunt's shop.

Her sewing machine drawers were no longer meticulous like they used to be in her old shop, as if she no longer cared. The buttons, bobbins, hooks and eyes, clasps, pins, and chalks all dumped in the drawers, some choking with loose tangled threads. I dragged out the boxes, paper patterns, and folded fabrics from under her worktable and flipped through them. Corner to corner, I went through the shop like an army of ants but after I'd finished I was empty-handed.

I went to the kitchen space and looked all around. Nothing hidden there. Next and the final place: our common room where the rickety old chest was the sole occupant.

I started with the bottom drawers, then the second row, then the third. I stood on tiptoe for the third row of drawers where Aunt kept her old purses. The purses were stiff from disuse, leathers falling away at the corners, the clasps tarnished to greyish-brown, some bags stuck together. I opened them one by one. Empty, empty, empty. Then, the last purse, at the very back of the drawer, felt a bit lumpy to the touch. I took it out.

Inside the purse was a neat stack of Mom's letters: seven blue, thrice folded airmail letters with the USA postage stamp marks on each. My inner ears whammed like a factory engine in full gear and my mouth went dry. The letters seemed to glow in my hands. I brought them to my nose; no smell of Mom, only of the old musty purse. I rushed to open a letter but stopped; this wasn't the way. I had waited too many years for this moment; I must savour it. I put the letters in date order, the oldest on top, the most recent at the bottom. It wasn't easy to do as some stamped dates were not clear.

It was almost seven years since she had left. Reading Mom's earlier letters I learned she had two girls and had suffered two miscarriages. The miscarriages were boys, she thought, at least the first one, for sure. She was pregnant again, and very much wanted it to be a boy. Having a boy was a Korean wife's duty, but she took that duty to America where no one cared and with no Koreans to shame her. And how many times could a woman give birth? I worried that she could be torn in half. Her mother-in-law, a tall, strait-laced devout Catholic lady, accepted Mom and was kindness itself, but Mom doubted if her kindness extended to her past mistake. They lived in the in-law's basement, so she was keeping me as a secret until they could afford their own home. Her father-in-law was an English teacher, and John, her husband, was finishing up his civil engineering degree, working part time in a large construction firm. Mom found adjusting to a new country, a new family, and new customs more difficult than she had imagined, and worried that she might never get used to it. Her proud, much-prized English when she was in Korea turned out to be woefully inadequate when talking with native speakers.

She was always aware of being a foreigner. "I'm glad that Su-young's doing well, I hope she's not too much of a burden," she wrote at the end of each letter, like a sign off, like a coda after a long symphony.

Mom's uncertainty and her tenuous position distressed me. I wanted her to be as I always remembered —sunny, beautiful, confident, commanding every room she entered. It was selfish but I couldn't survive here with the image of Mom as fragile, insecure, and sad; I would have nothing left to hold on to.

I wanted to believe that she missed me as I missed her, that she could never put all of her feelings into this stingy little airmail letter. Because, like me, once she started, her bottled-up longing would break open like a collapsing dam and drown her. So, she had to hide me away, taking me out only when no one was looking. She knew I had no place among the blond haired, fair-skinned people, just like she hadn't. Maybe that was why she never wrote to me directly. Instead, she kept having babies, to make a clan of her own, so she could feel a belonging. She'd found her own safe nest, but a nest only large enough for her and John's brood.

She mentioned the packages she sent: "Did the sweaters fit? What about the red coat? She must be big by now. I did my best to guess her size. If they don't fit, sell them, you should get good money." I never saw any such clothes.

The next letter revealed a bit more of her financial state: "Please look out for money coming to you. I'm sorry it's late this time. Money is tight. I am looking for a job but with two kids and another on the way, it's hard."

One unusually long letter was dated two years earlier. She said thoughts about me were affecting her life. She wasn't sure anymore if it was missing me or the guilt of leaving me behind. Some days, a simple falling leaf made her weep, which began worrying John. They were saving money but not fast enough. Then one day, an incident in the grocery store brought everything out:

Mom and her mother-in-law were shopping. In one of the aisles, a little girl was crying, lost, looking for her mother. Mom ran to her, and clasping the girl into her arms, Mom began wailing uncontrollably; the girl was terrified in the grip of a stranger. Her mother showed up and prised her daughter out from Mom's clutch. Mom, crouched in the corner, carried on sobbing, calling my name over and over. People were gathering, the manager was called, while her mother-in-law was horrified at such a display in public. Later that evening, John told his parents about me. To Mom's surprise, they were sympathetic, chastising her for keeping me a secret all that time.

Then, I held the final letter to read and my knees gave way. I was going to America! They had sent money for my airline ticket and immigration process. They were very expensive, but John had sold his prized stamp collection he'd started as a child. Mom thought it'd take six months to process my immigration papers and passport, but by then, John would finish his degree and be working full time; they'd move to a house of their own, large enough to include me. She hadn't forgotten the piano she promised me, perhaps it would come for my first birthday with them. She said my baby sisters were excited, especially the oldest one, Carina, who was only five but already acting fifteen—gentle, loving, and wise beyond her years. How beautiful her name sounded. I read and re-read it. But something was not right. I turned the letter over—it was dated more than a year ago. An entire year had passed without me ever knowing of its content. The one thing, the only thing I had been waiting for came and went, without a peep from Aunt. I felt faint. I heard myself making a weird, gurgling sound. I thought I'd go mad. I looked at the date again, retracing the time: it just about coincided with that night when Aunt took In-sook and me for the after-dinner stroll, bought us those sticky buns, promised me my tuition. All that while, she was padding her pocket, spending my going-away money. And now, I was stuck here for good.

But, where were the more recent letters? Wouldn't Mom have asked how the immigration was going? When was I expected? What excuse did Aunt give? Where were the recent letters? I rushed back to the cupboard to look for them.

"What are you looking at?" a soft voice enquired.

I jumped with a screech, taken by surprise. Kang-jin ambled into the room, and closing the door behind him, he snatched the letter I was holding. He smiled; no surprise on his face, so he knew it too. He picked up Aunt's old purse.

"Isn't this my mother's purse? And these letters. Humm, they're all addressed to her. Did she say you could read them? Like did she give you permission?" He hit my head with the purse, not hard, just enough to show his disapproval.

Why wasn't he at the hospital with the others, was my first thought.

"Let's first put these back into the purse exactly as you found them," he said.

I gathered the letters and put them back into the purse, my anger taking a backseat, alert at the possible, imminent violence.

"Where are my mother's makeup things? She's staying with father overnight at the hospital; she wants them. Can you get them for me?"

I took out her makeup basket from the bottom chest drawer, bagged it with a cloth and brought it to him.

Kang-jin sat down, leisurely, looked at me again, then at Aunt's purse.

"So, now you know. You're *not* going to America. Not anytime soon. It took your mom over five years to send for you, didn't it? It'll be a long time before she can do it again. Money, money — she's got no money. You aren't going anywhere. Get that in to your head."

Hitting my head again for emphasis he continued, "Now, about you going through her things, what do we do about that? What do you think I should do? I'll tell you what. Let's keep it a secret, just between you and me. Your Aunt will never find out. You can trust me. See? Now we have something between us. From now on if you ever need anything, or need to talk, you come to me, alright?"

What nonsense; would I ask a starving wolf to shield me? Still, it was unnerving to hear him talk this way, like a cat toying with a mouse. I wanted to run for the door, but he was in the way.

"I'm tired, aren't you?" he said, slinking down on his back. "Ahhh, there. So good. Come, lie next to me. Let's take a nap." He tapped the floor next to him. I didn't move. He grabbed my wrist and yanked me down. I laid down, all my senses a live-wire; I didn't know what was worse, obeying him or defying him. Supporting his head with an arm, he turned to face me. He lifted my top, peeked at my chest.

"You mom was a real looker, you know that?" He tried to unbutton my top. I shot up. He twisted my wrist, forcing me back down. "Stop fidgeting. Don't move, you'll just get hurt. You don't want to play hard to get."

He squeezed my breast. It hurt. I tried to take his hand away; he smacked my head, then circled his hand around my nipple slowly and pinched it.

"Like that? I bet even your mom's tits aren't as good as these. Close your eyes and relax . . . feel . . . you'll enjoy it more. . . . I know you, known you all my life. You're made for this, waiting for this. You'll want more after. You just ask and I'll always give it to you."

He grabbed my inner thigh and forced my legs open, his breathing getting faster and shallower. I fought him. *Whack.* He punched my stomach, knocking the breath out of me. He jumped on top of me, his arm pushing into my collarbone, his handsome face turning gargoyle-like.

"Lay still and open your legs. This time, I'll get what I want. I always wanted to get into her, but I'll settle for you. So give me all you've got like she would." My mind went blank, my body too. I stopped moving. I'd have stopped breathing if I could. His forearm pressing on my throat, he pulled down my skirt and underwear, and unzipped himself. The zipper scraped deep along my thigh as he pushed his pants down to his knees. A sharp pain shot through me. I urged myself to stop fighting. "Let it go, let him be . . . Don't fight . . ." I repeated. I went limp.

Then it happened again. I flew up from my body. "No, no, no. Don't leave. Don't go. If you go now, you won't find your way back," I begged. This time, my leaving my body felt final. "Don't float away . . . Stay, stay. This'll pass if we just keep still . . . that's all we have to do . . . just hold on . . . we'll figure it out later . . . stay. Just stay," and on I fought with my floating self. But I was already above me, looking down from the ceiling: Kang-jin on top of my body, a gigantic sea monster thrashing, raging destruction, and I, the bottom of the ocean, unmoving, unfeeling, waiting for the storm to pass.

Kang-jin had left. The room was quiet but my head roared, my legs splayed apart, my inner thighs and pelvis covered in sticky, bloody, slimy wetness.

• • •

Our shack was lit up.

It meant Mi-hae and In-sook were back home from their dinner with Jae-in. The night had swallowed up the day, and soon the curfew sirens would blow, forcing everyone inside. Rain fell. I sat on the street curb in front of our shack, not wanting to go back in. Raucous laughter, chattering and singing from the brothel next door filled the otherwise quiet night. A drunken man stumbled out from the brothel. Holding himself up with his forehead against the door frame, he urinated onto our adjoining wall. A young girl, about my age, as small and scrawny as me, sashayed out, looking for her customer. Having finished peeing, her customer was flailing his arms, having lost balance. The girl deftly hoisted him up, exposing her white armpit under her short Korean dress top, like a lewd grin. She cooed into his ear, giggling, swinging her hips suggestively against the man's thigh as they walked back in. But before stepping into her brothel, the girl turned and looked me up and down, her dark, painted red lips curled up in a sneer. Such a young face, but her gaze was cold, hard, and impossibly old. Still a teenager, she was already a practiced whore and would be a whore till she couldn't be any more.

I quickly turned my head away, as if I didn't see her, as if she didn't merit my gaze, as if by merely looking at her, I was dirtying myself. I shivered, not from the cold or the rain, but from the realisation of the meaning of her blatant confrontational look: I could be her. She and I were not that far apart. Just a matter of time before I become like her, if things continued on this way. What if I didn't pass the high school entrance exam? And even if I passed, what if Aunt said no to my tuition. Did it even matter anymore? I was soiled, no longer pure; Mom farther away than ever. How could I even face her. I wanted to cry but crying would bring self-pity; self-pity hinted at hope, hope for justice, hope for a helping hand.

The curfew siren blew, whirling, sharp, and distinct, same as it did last night and the night before and before. But I was not the same; I wasn't a girl anymore.

Chapter Twenty-One

I pinch the pale green bottom of an acacia flower and pull it from its pistil. When a drop of sweet dew gathers at its tube-like end, I suck it out. The subtle, fragrant sweetness flutters around my tongue, making me want more. I am so ravenous I could swallow a tree. I rip out another flower head, suck at it, then another and another, until the ground is covered with the carcasses of severed flowers.

I squint to look up at Lee; the sun behind her blindingly bright, as she gorges on acacia nectar. Our hands are a sticky mess. I laugh at Lee, flower petals stuck all over her face. She laughs back, pointing at my face. But she mustn't laugh at me: I am never messy. I get right up to her and stand on tiptoes, for she's much taller than me. I pick the petals off of her face. She keeps still, letting me. But the more I pluck them off, the thicker the layers become, soon covering her whole face, even the eyes, nose, and mouth.

Frantic, I work to free her of flowers. I am afraid she can't breathe, but she looks peaceful like a standing Buddha made of blossoms. She smells heavenly. I know that smell: Mom's smell. I peel away faster; Mom's inside. Get her out. I claw at the flowers. But I don't see Mom, no Lee either, just more flowers. Soon the ground is littered with petals. The ground seems to be moving. I look closer; the petals are twitching, quivering, turning into wriggling white larvae. They writhe and torque their bodies up, onto my feet, up to my ankles and calves. My legs are covered with them. I stamp my feet to get them off, but I am losing balance. I am no longer standing on Earth but in a sea of squirming maggots.

"Su-young-ah, wake up!" Someone was shaking my leg and patting my face. Aunt was looking down at me. I was glad to get away from the crawling maggots.

"You're thrashing like a drowning person. Come, let's eat. It's been over a week, you lying here, moping about. Please don't you get me worked up. I've already got one invalid. Enough is enough. Sit up and eat this porridge." Aunt put her arm around my shoulders, propping me up against the wall, her staccato persistence wearing me out.

I didn't want to see our peeling walls, the leaky ceiling, or worry about our old chest collapsing any day. I didn't want to pop those ever-present lice between my thumb nails, or see their tiny egg-beads embedded along the edge of our blankets, pillows, even our undershirts, hatching, as itchy as acid. I didn't want to wander around the streets, long after the school and library had closed. Most of all, I didn't know how to erase Kang-jin's attack. It was easier to lay here in my corner, taking a break from all the negotiating—where, what, and whom to avoid. Being sick was my refuge. And the night too; the night was mine when I could vomit the silent screams of my day's shame and dread, and let the darkness swallow me up. Crying into the pillow cleansed me, it kept me sane.

Aunt held out a bowl of rice gruel. I reached for the spoon, and dropped it. It weighed a ton. She picked it up and asked, "Su-young-ah. Will it make you feel better if you wrote to your mom?"

My foggy brain caught that. It'd been a long time since I wrote to her. But there was no point really, because Aunt was always there, watching what I wrote—the happy, smart teenage daughter sending her mom cheerful greetings.

"If you eat up everything in the bowl, you can write to her."

She fed me and I ate. She went out to fetch the pencil and paper.

On the other side of the room, Uncle was sitting up too, his blank face staring in my direction. I could end up like him, I thought. Aunt came back. She told me to write that I'd been sick for weeks and need medicine and a special doctor, too. Please send money. "Let's hope this will get us some money." She walked out with my letter.

Whenever I got sick like this, it felt as if it was all in my head. Nothing really hurt, everything hurt; I opened my eyes, it was day; I opened my eyes again, it was night, with light and dark repeating endlessly; then the dark side dragged me down to its blackness. Sometimes that blackness turned into an uphill alleyway where I was being chased, but I couldn't make headway because the alleyway turned into a swamp and my feet were bound with stones. Other times the blackness was the room where I was lying; a small balloon floated into the room, bouncing along wall to wall, happy, happy, bounce, bounce, and as it did, it got bigger and bigger, sucking the air out of the room; soon the balloon got so big, it took up the entire room, extending to every corner of it, squashing me beneath it, squeezing out my breaths, choking me with its monstrous body.

I'm back at the old church backyard. I look for the same spot where Lee was because Mom's there. But the church backyard has turned into Mr. Chang's, a steep hill going down, like the church's, but smaller and scragglier. The last time I saw Mr. Chang was with Mom at her army camp. Funny how his dilapidated shack still looks the same after all these years. And look, his son, Gombo Oppa, is walking towards me, smiling the same glad smile, from his squinting eyes down to his wide-open arms, ready to hold me.

"Su-young-ah. I've been waiting for you. How pretty you've grown."

He swoops me up and swirls me around; I'm dizzy but giggling, too, at the spinning houses, trees and the sky, as if I am still seven years old. But I'm surprised his face is smooth, handsome even: the deep pockmarks on his face, giving his nickname, Gombo, are all gone. What do I call him now that he no longer has gombo marks? He turns around and squats in front of me, offering me a piggyback ride. I jump on his back. Nimbly he runs down the hill just like we used to. He doesn't complain how heavy I've become: I am fourteen now, all grown up, don't you know. As we go back up the hill, I am smiling because he says the same old thing he used to say. So I do too.

"Su-young-ah. Oppa will always love you."

"Till you die?"

"Till I die."

"What about after you die?"

"Even after I die."

"And carry me on your back?"

"Yes."

"And why?"

"So your feet won't ever get dirty."

"Even when you're a famous painter?"

"Even then. You'll be famous too, for everyone will know your face from my paintings. . . ."

How strange. We all know Gombo Oppa had killed himself years ago, at age eighteen. But here he is, just as we were, except without pockmarks. He had been accepted into the famous art school, Hong-Ik University, but Mr. Chang said, never. "Artists are lazy hoodlums not fit for real life. They all die from starvation or as opium addicts. You won't be wasting my hard earned money. You are a disgrace!" They fought and fought. Finally Gombo Oppa gave up. But he didn't want to live without his art. His father found him hanging from the tall tree in their backyard. There wasn't even a funeral I could go to.

• • •

"Su-young-ah, wake up. Yumi is here. Don't you want to say hello?" Aunt said. Yumi was looking down at me, half smiling, half grimacing.

"Su-young-ah, what's happened to you? You look so thin. Are you alright?" She took out her crisply ironed, white handkerchief I always envied and tapped at her tearful eyes. "Everyone says hello and wants you to get well soon. Miss Go, too." Yumi put a bundle of get-well notes in my hands. "And our upcoming concert, what a mess we are in. We've no soloist. If you don't get better soon, Hae-ra will be singing your solo. Remember her, the girl from America? Who knew she could sing. But she's not you, she sings like the way she looks, wobbly, no bite, no flavour. Oh, she wants you to get better too, she doesn't want the blame if we do badly, haha. With Miss Jung gone, you gone, it's no fun at all."

At the mention of chorus and Miss Jung, I tried to get up but Yumi held me down.

"Just get better, and quick. School's boring without you. Everything's a bore. My mom and my sisters are asking about you, too. Mom says she will make you your favourite potato stew. Remember her stew?"

To be honest, her stew was alright. What I really loved were the potatoes—their homely yet subtle, irresistible taste. I loved them so much that Mom once threatened to marry me to a potato farmer. I said, "No, Mom. I'm going to make a lot of money and have all the potatoes I want, and all the other things too!"

It was strange to hear people needing me, when I didn't even want me or need me. After Yumi left, I felt the desire to get well, but I couldn't stand up. My legs looked as if all the fluids had been drained out; my knees protruded out like fists, two sticks of bones coming down from the knees to ankles; the skin around the bones hung loose and swung side to side. Still I noticed one thing: even as I gave up to my illnesses and the onslaught of blackness, something deep inside me always watched me and tethered me to it, something that couldn't be squashed or broken. It wasn't loud or even large, but it was always there, this tiny thing inside me pulsing and watchful. Now it nudged me and said it wasn't time to disappear yet, there were still things waiting. I listened. And I slowly sat up.

Chapter Twenty-Two

Yumi and I had been inseparable even before elementary school. She lived only a few doors away from us. Yumi limped, only slightly, from polio. That slight limp would become an insurmountable handicap when she came into marrying age. When we lived in the old house, very little went unnoticed in our tight neighbourhood. Everything and everyone was under a magnifying glass: dissected, interpreted and talked about at length. A kindly neighbour looking at Yumi's leg might worry, "Tsk, tsk, tsk, the poor thing, who's ever going to take her for a wife." Others dismissed her as if her life was already over. But Yumi never felt it. Her parents doted on her and protected her, especially from us—the neighbourhood kids. Yumi's mom used to invite us kids over to play in her home, treating us with snacks to get us on her side, so we wouldn't openly make fun of her. Still, kids called Yumi "mismatch chopsticks" behind her back, a deep insult because who would use two different sized chopsticks? Not even the poorest person would. God help the young bride who was careless enough to put a mismatching pair on a dinner table.

Polio or not, Yumi was fearless. She played straight, hard, and never cheated. I liked her for that and we bonded right away. We used to hang on the exercise bar by our knees, looking at the world upside down, waiting and waiting for the others to fall. We competed on the seesaw, trying to out jump each other—quite scary, as her balance wasn't good, but she got angry if any of us went easy on her.

We used to sneak into the manhwa store, the Korean comic bookstore, hoarding the newest serials under our seats, devouring them, forgetting time. Proper young girls wouldn't be caught in a dark, rickety manhwa store, sitting elbow to elbow with smelly boys. Aunt didn't approve, she said manhwa turned kids' brains into garbage and the manhwa store was a breeding ground for hooligans. But Yumi's mom would rent out an entire serial and let us read in her home. She wanted Yumi home, safe, and happy. She'd often sit with us, doing her chores, and from time to time, she'd pat Yumi's bottom with such affection that even I felt the warmth and contentment.

While Aunt's tailoring shop failed, and we had to move to the poorer section of Mapo, Yumi's father's pawnshop flourished, and they moved to a wealthier area of Mapo—still just a longish walk between us.

During holiday seasons when the demand for her father's pawnshop spiked, her father worked late. Then Yumi and I brought him hot dinners her mom prepared. His shop in Jong-ro District was like a natural history museum. It had carvings made of marble and jade; a stuffed peacock in full feather display; a rug made of an entire tiger, his menacing jaw raised up, ready to devour; a Japanese samurai sword, its handle with inlaid gold, depicting a serene crane in full flight, a sword that served no other purpose than to kill, yet made with such devotion and artistry; and masks, both Korean and Japanese—they were grotesque and fascinating at the same time. The fearsome looking Korean masks felt as though they were carved in one broad stroke capturing a single essence of swirling energy, but they also held a wink, as if to burst into laughter. But Japanese masks looked serious even when laughing. Their white faces, exquisitely detailed, were sinister and ghostly, belonging more in the dark, cold underworld.

When we got out of his shop, Yumi and I walked holding hands through the night streets, and with the pocket money her father gave us, we treated ourselves to spicy rice cakes and fish cakes on sticks in savoury broths that burned our tongues, making us stomp our feet as the warm broths glided all the way down to our toes.

Yumi and I were almost fifteen. Although she was taller than me, our classmates called us "the twins." She was the first person I'd confide in and ask for help, but this time, I wasn't sure. The minute I told her about Kang-jin, everything would change between us. Our friendship would effectively be over; she would never look at me the same way again; I'd turn from a friend to a charity case, someone to be pitied and helped. And her mom would separate us to protect Yumi's purity. They could accept my being poor, practically an orphan, even a bastard, but not being sexually impure. It was the pit every parent feared their young daughter would fall into. We didn't talk about boys, let alone sex. Yes, we sneaked in magazines that told love stories, and we loved reading about clandestine letter exchanges, a furtive handholding in the dark, even an embrace! But nothing close to what Kang-jin did was ever mentioned in the story. We went to separate schools for boys and girls. We were taught to put away our curiosity about sex until university, when we came of age to marry. Dating, too, was for university students. If you walked holding hands with a boy, he'd better be your younger brother or an elderly relative. Otherwise, you could be suspended from school. In a case like mine, expelled. There were boys at our church and even in my church choir. But we kept our distance, even if we liked a certain boy. I never even heard of a girl of my age having my kind of trouble.

"Don't talk about your difficult past. Don't show your weakness. They'll only use it against you, laugh behind your back," Aunt had advised Mom before she left for America. She was right: all I would get is pity and mockery, like they mocked Yumi's legs.

A circle was drawn, with me inside. If I kept quiet, no one could drag me out, shining a light on me, gossiping, disguised as help. So I would keep everything to myself and find a way to fly out of this circle, alone. I didn't know how, yet.

• • •

"Yumi-ya, come to my room; help me get into my new dress. I don't understand it. It fitted me perfectly when I bought it but not anymore. And please get ready. Dad's coming home soon with his dinner guests," her mom said, through the shoji door. It was time for me leave, leave their warm and merry home. It also meant I might go without dinner tonight. Yumi's mom was always generous, her large body matching her big heart. But no matter how generous, she couldn't invite me to stay for the dinner with their important guests.

Whenever I was with them and dinnertime came, without asking, Yumi's mom would put an extra pair of chopsticks and a heaped up bowl of rice on the table. If anyone in that household felt sorry for me, they never showed it. Often I went to their home just to have something good to eat. These days, I pushed the limits of their welcome, staying late and often.

On my way out, the smell of grilling beef patties and fragrant sesame oil sautéing vegetables wafted onto their courtyard. My stomach wanted to stay. Perhaps I could go into the kitchen and say hello to one of the nice housekeepers and say how delicious it all smelled .... but I forced myself to leave.

From Yumi's home to our shack took less than fifteen minutes to walk, but the contrast from her block to ours was always startling. As soon as I turned a few quiet alleyways, her wealthy neighbourhood gave way to our hectic road, where shops of all shapes and means popped up almost daily. Our shack stood further below.

I wondered if there would be food at home tonight. Even after the big to-do of Jae-in's family linking up with ours, nothing much changed; our poverty still dug deep. Uncle returned from the hospital without improvement, except for getting a name to his illness — a stroke, and beyond recovery.

When I got home, I faced an unusually steamy and lively dinner, with the nauseating smell that made me choke. Aunt, In-sook, and Mi-hae were hunched over the low table, chewing and making lip-smacking noises. In-sook scooted over for me to join in. A large pot sat in the middle of our low table. Globules of glistening fat floated on a dirty, watery soup. Bloated chicken claws with their wrinkly skin and nails intact stuck out from the broth. From the opposite side, a chicken's head floated, including its beak, a blueish cloudy eyeball staring up. Some clean chicken bones were piled up on the side of the table. Aunt had bought the chicken on credit from the landlord and boiled the entire thing in water, not even a clove of garlic to mask its thick noxious smell. I got up, saying I wasn't hungry.

Aunt shouted after me, tearing at a chicken wing, "You arrogant bitch. You think you're too good for this. . . . You haven't suffered enough, that's what. You don't know what real hunger is yet. Get out of here!"

I covered up my nausea.

"And one of these days, I'll cut off that nose of yours. Sensitive like a pregnant woman, can't stand you going around smelling things all the time. It's all the same once it goes into your stomach!" she yelled after me.

I sat on my usual street curb, wanting fresh air, but the smell of stale alcohol and rancid pork fat drifted out from the whorehouse, adding to my already nervous stomach. I stood up, shaking it off. Just then, what Aunt said pinged in my head, "Sensitive like a pregnant woman." I had heard of pregnant women retching at the smell of certain food, making everyone jump for joy at the tell tale sign. I counted the days since my last period. Being sick and all, I'd completely forgotten. I was over two weeks late. Everything in front of me went black.

Chapter Twenty-Three

"Hey, you, student! Time to get off, my shift's done!" the driver hollered.

I woke up in an empty bus.

"Done for the day, another day gone, how time goes, look at that, have you ever seen such a clear sky. Is that a spring sky? You can always sniff spring, yeah, even in the dead of winter. But where's my spring... this useless life of mine, can't live, can't die," he muttered, then looking at my befuddled state through his rear view mirror, he yelled again, "and what are you doing in my bus all day? Why aren't you in school? You a real student or you steal that uniform? If you wanna sleep, go home and sleep, how I envy you kids, sleeping anywhere, anytime. I was like that once too."

He lumbered out of the bus.

I looked out to the parking lot, it was blanketed with empty buses. I'd never been here before. I got off, and weaving through the buses, I reached a small station office at the back of the lot. The clock said one in the afternoon. When I asked where I was, the lone man at the desk tilted his head to the destination plaque behind him. The plaque said Jang-an Dong, the far eastern stretches of Seoul. It would take an hour or two to walk back. I'd been walking all morning until I couldn't walk any more, then I'd got on the bus, using all the money that I had, to nurse my feet and think without thinking about where to go next. I was people watching and street watching as the bus went back and forth east and west. And all the while, the worries in my mind jumped around, badgering me, "What are we going to do? What are *you* going to do? Have you got any plans?" I hadn't, none at all.

I was petrified. I knew a little from my schoolbook about the process of pregnancy, but it was so basic and abstract I couldn't get my head around it. The subject being taboo, the schoolbook explained it in one paragraph, and our teacher left it as a simple reference, never explaining it to us, or it could be that I'd skipped the class that day. If I gathered enough courage to ask Aunt or even Yumi's mom, they'd ask me right back: "What a thing to ask, why do you want to know, why are you wasting time thinking about such a thing, what are you up to, you'll know it soon enough when you get married, your head should be only on books." And then I'd have put them on an alert. They'd watch and suspect me.

So I waited for winter vacation to end, as if school would magically erase my worries. But when I went back to school, I couldn't go through the gate. I walked away. I didn't belong there any more. I couldn't face my classmates' innocent chatters, all the fretting about passing the high school exam meaningless. The only thing that I kept asking: how can I disappear, not to another place, not even to Mom, not anymore, but disappear as if I were never born? Of course these thoughts were not new, as I often had them ever since Mom left. Now that desire stomped its feet, impatient for me to get it done. But how does one get unborn? So I gathered a list of options.

One: Fall from a pedestrian bridge into the on-coming traffic. Cars were still a new phenomenon, and drivers were notorious for not yielding to pedestrians. Large streets got barricaded to steer people onto the bridge. We saw the warning posters of car accident victims everywhere, even on the sides of the buses, depicting cracked skulls and gooey, tofu-coloured brain matter spilling out, surrounded by bright red blood. An effective warning. A nightmarish way to die. Then, some people fell from the bridge intentionally.

Two: I could jump into the Han River. But I heard that the city would come knocking at our shack, demanding Aunt pay the cost of cleaning up the pollution; she'd curse at me, dead or not. So many people jumped into the Han River to die that it became an environmental hazard. Besides, I didn't want to turn into a water ghost.

Three: Hanging. This felt physically difficult to accomplish, needing preparation of where, when and how.

Four: The most attractive option: carbon monoxide poisoning. All Koreans, rich and poor, had a unique underground heating system with coal called "Ondol." But sometimes deadly carbon monoxide seeped through broken flooring and into the room where people slept, killing many each winter—people said it was painless, you just never woke up. Its simplicity and a lack of drama appealed to me, except for one drawback: someone was always in our shack. No matter how hateful they were, I couldn't kill them with me. So I was back to zero. These thoughts had been looping around and around all morning as I walked and sat in the bus.

Walking homeward from the bus station, I detoured to the old churchyard. Acacia branches looked like heads of tangled hair in this mild January. The whole of Mapo District came into view below my feet. Every few months, its landscape changed, new buildings gobbling up old ones, erasing any trace of the post-war poverty. Soon they would come for our street, bulldozing our brave little shack, the brothel and all. I wondered where we'd live then. But it wouldn't matter, I most likely wouldn't be alive to care.

Standing on the edge of the cliff, I thought of hollering like Lee did years ago—that gave her the courage to leave Aunt, but that felt childish now. I plopped down on the dirt, my eyes fixed on the deep, endless, pitiless clear sky that no cloud dared come near. The wind changed. A strange smell filled the air. I looked up and across the church property. Black smoke rose up from the far end of a barren and abandoned field. I went over to explore.

Two men sat on plastic bins facing the township below, their backs to me. They were smoking, drinking and chatting. To their right, they put up a spit of two wooden forks, about two metres apart with a long stick sitting on top. On that stick, a mid-sized dog was skewered from its mouth to its rump, his neck straining, stretched to the limit by the thick stick staking through it. His face was a tiny bulb of a thing, recognisable only by his ears pointing up. His four legs splayed, looking indecent and painful, his outer skin burnt charcoal black, his sharp teeth jutting out from his bare jawbones like some monster in a horror film. The fire below crackled from the fat dribbling down from his head. His taut, blackened skin split open, cracking like parched land in a drought. Blood oozed from the ripped skin. Rivers of red streaks dripped into the hissing fire, causing an unbearably vile smell. Black smoke swirled upward, menacing, mesmerising, expanding into the sky, spoiling the clear blueness of it, like a kid with a crayon smearing a white sheet of paper.

I was disgusted but couldn't look away. I held my nose.

One man turned around and saw me.

"You hungry? Want some?"

But the other one nudged him urgently, pointing to the street below.

"Look, down there. Another demo!"

Both got up, and walked to the edge of the cliff, craning their necks to get a full view. I followed them, and looked down.

"Wow. This is no little popup protest. This is the biggest demo yet," the taller one said.

Mobs of students were streaming into the boulevard from side streets and alleyways, high school students with their easy-to-identify black and white uniforms, mixed in with plain-clothed university students. Opposite them, the police gathered, forming rows of neat horizontal lines. They wore helmets and protective gear and held plastic shields and long sticks.

"These crazy young bastards. Their parents kill themselves to get them into a good school, and all they want is to get killed. For what? Think Park Chung-Hee will give up his power just because they wave their arms, scream and protest? I bet Park will stay on to become an emperor. Why not? He's already changed his two terms to three. Why not go all the way? I would if I had the army and newspapers behind me."

"Can't blame the Japanese any more. Can't blame the Americans, either. We're all we've got. So let's fight it out among ourselves ... Give 'em good you poor bastards. I'm rooting for ya!" the shorter one bellowed.

Orderly and measured, the students marched, carrying large banners and chanting: "Students Coalition Against Park Chung-Hee!" "No More Dictatorship!" But when they got near the lines of police, they slowed, bucking at the sight of the impenetrable wall of protective shields and gear. The front row of students came to a stop and began weaving in and out as the crowd behind them continued to push forward. Someone in the back threw a rock towards the police. Then another. Soon, rocks were pelting them. Some police ducked, their blockade unravelling. With sudden momentum and a loud battle cry, the students plunged forward. The police struggled to keep their stance, shields up, ready to use the sticks if necessary. The police threw a warning tear gas canister into the crowd. The students scattered, but came back, even more frenzied, throwing more rocks. More tear gas that left thick squiggly lines in the air before covering the boulevard with grey smoke. The smoke rose all the way up to us, mixing with the roasting dog's smoke. The combined stench was horrible.

I knew the tear gas smell, that garlicky, peppery sting, and the tearing, coughing, and nose running. Although as middle schoolers we didn't participate in these demonstrations, sometimes we got caught up in them unaware—the wrong place at the wrong time. We heard whispers of students being killed, hit by tear gas canisters.

Suddenly, days of crushing lethargy left my body. I

became ecstatic. All the debates on how to die and the fear of it fell away. This was it: a street filled with demonstrators and tear gas. This was the perfect setting.

I ran out of the churchyard, down to the street, fighting upstream against students running away. I pushed my way onto the boulevard, into the thicket of bodies. I would disappear into the chaos of screams, smoke, confusion, violence. I felt wildly alive, almost giddy. I put my schoolbag in between my feet and stood still, letting people hit and shove me. In seconds, I had difficulty seeing and breathing. My nose ran, throat burned, eyes teared, but I wanted more, much more—I wanted to be knocked out of my consciousness and be dead. Smoke blanketed everything. I could barely see a person in front of me. A shoulder struck me, a foot kicked the back of my knee. I stumbled forward. I grabbed at a moving body in front but fell to the ground instead. A shoe stepped on me. More assaults. I let everything fall on me. I felt peaceful in the whirl of madness.

A momentary quiet followed, and people scattered away. Then, just a few feet away, I saw a pair of mismatching legs. It had to be Yumi. I looked up; I recognised her long body shape. I called her, but my throat burned. I crawled closer. Yumi's sleeve was torn off from her arm, blood flowing. Hae-ra was next to her, holding Yumi up. Hae-ra was crying, calling for her mom. She probably didn't know which way to go; she didn't live in this area like Yumi and I did. I went for them. Someone shoved me again. I fell. I crawled again. Yumi had passed out, her face red and swollen, eyes shut. I held her bleeding arm; the moving crowd kept pulling us apart. Hae-ra and I struggled to stay together, holding schoolbags and carrying Yumi. Finally we got off the boulevard and escaped into an alleyway.

Hae-ra later told me that school had ended early due to the demonstration alert. Despite the danger, they were fascinated by the spectacle and got swept up in it.

I had run into the demonstration to get killed, but I ended up taking care of Yumi at the hospital. And that evening I got my period.

Chapter Twenty-Four

Yumi and I never talked about our periods, it went under the same taboo heading as sex. In-sook, who was older than me, didn't warn me either, and Mi-hae, I didn't expect her to. As if by a silent consent, all women went about their days never mentioning it, never showing their ordeal or suffering from the cramps. Or it could be I was dense and unaware. When I first got mine, I was sure that I was dying of some very shameful disease. So many ways to die, and I was going to die bleeding from the unmentionable place, surely having to do with my being born bad. Aunt was the only person I could confess to. "Oh, already? All grown up, aren't you. Don't worry, you aren't dying any time soon. You're a woman now, that's all," she said, handing me some pieces of rough fabric and two big safety pins. I was to use and reuse them month after month—every scrap of cloth precious. No matter how many times and how hard I scrubbed the cloth, the stain and the stiffness never went away, chafing my inner thighs, the folds threatening to fall out, making me walk like a duck.

Now with my period back, I got my life back. The effect was immediate: I no longer minded our crumbling shack, Aunt's cursing sounded endearing, and I welcomed the shooting pains. I was a schoolgirl again, and my envy of my classmates lifted too. I'd been jealous of their carefree ways, their unblemished, pure Korean girlishness.

I went back to school with a different attitude: I wanted to get into a high school, any high school, and once again find a way to Mom. I suspected I was at least two or three grades behind, especially in maths and science. Just figuring out how much I didn't know took time, bogging me down. I kept going back and back till I found out I had to start again from the seventh grade, a whole two years behind. I borrowed Yumi's old textbooks as Aunt had sold mine. They had been bought used in the first place. My classmates had been studying for the entrance exam from the first year of our middle school; these intense and relentless studies didn't end until we passed the university entrance exam. Only then, could we finally breathe easier.

I began pulling all-nighters with In-sook. Although annoyed at first, because she thought I was being a copycat, she gave in and we ended up liking studying together, two soldiers in a battle. I stayed on even after In-sook finished her studies; I loved these long stretches of quiet nights where my mind buzzed with sharp focus. I regretted the years wasted moping about, feeling victimised, when all along the best escape was right in front of me.

To my surprise, I loved maths. It was intimidating in the beginning, but once I began from basic algebra, step by step, everything became logical and clear. There was only one possible answer to any given maths problem. If I memorised and followed the steps and formulas faithfully, one correct answer waited at the end of the labyrinth of numbers and figures. How beautiful was that! Like a piece of music, right and wrong clear, no grey numbers tugging and pulling, freaking you out, like in real life.

● ● ●

"Kim Su-young. Where is Kim Su-young?" Miss Go asked at our morning roll call. I ducked, but her voice knew where I was: "Come to my desk at lunch. Don't fail me this time." Everyone turned to look at me, whispering. Being called to the teacher's hall usually meant one thing: Trouble. Of course I knew why. Her patience had run out. I was a bad student, poor academically and unreliable with tuition. I was always late paying tuition fees, the worst offence. She was kind enough not to announce it to the entire class as she sometimes did when too many of us were late paying.

Miss Go's desk was at the far end of the teacher's hall, facing the school yard, rain beating down against her window. The hall was empty except for a couple of teachers who were still at their desks.

She peered at me over her eyeglasses. "You haven't paid the last term, and you're late with this one. I've asked you to bring your parent to school, you haven't done that either. You put me in a bad position. I'm sorry to tell you but the school is giving you a notice. You have until the end of the month, then you'll be let go."

"Please help me write to my Mom!" I blurted out.

"Help you—w*hat?*"

"Please! Help me write to my Mom. She lives in America."

Miss Go looked at me, incredulous. Knowing someone who lived in America was rare; people only heard of it happening to some other lucky people. We believed that anyone who went to America became instantly wealthy. And here I was, the poorest of the students, talking about a mom in America.

I pushed forward before she could accuse me of lying. I told her that I had no one else to ask . . . I needed to send a letter to Mom, but I didn't dare, because of Aunt . . .

Just mentioning Aunt, I lost control, ruining my appeal for help. I'd been planning a succinct, rational plea for Miss Go to write to Mom, to delay my getting expelled and to ask for Mom to send the tuition directly to school. And to send for me. Going to America was my only real solution. Instead, I rambled on, in between sobs and nose running, spilling out my entire last seven years in one go—about Aunt, the letters and monies Mom sent that she took away, how she kept me from leaving so she could get more money from Mom. I told her everything except about Kang-jin. I couldn't tell her that. She'd recoil as if I were a leper. My teeth chattered, I was freezing as if I had swallowed a bucketful of ice.

Miss Go didn't interrupt me, not once. When I stopped talking, she got out of her chair, put her handkerchief into my hand.

"I've never heard such a thing . . . You sure everything you told me is all true? Does anyone else know?"

I said Yumi and her family knew some.

"You can go now. Have Yumi come to see me, right away." Then she added, "Bring me your mom's address. And a telephone number she can call."

Lunch was over, the last students rushing back to the classrooms, squeezing under one umbrella, giggling, squealing as they do, trying not to get their spotless white collars wrinkly with rain spots. I sat in a downpour on a school bench; the lashing rain calmed me. I went over my talk with Miss Go in my head again and again. Then I realised I'd made a terrible mistake: I had exposed Aunt to an authority. What if Miss Go told the school authorities, and they told the police, and then . . . ? I never meant to say all those things, but I blabbered like a beggar telling a sob story. Aunt's ferocious face flashed in front of me, along with Kang-jin's. But you can't swallow back what's already spit out.

"Well, it's better this way. Now we'll see what's what," was all I could tell myself.

● ● ●

Aunt was sewing in her shop. No one else was home except Uncle in the main room. As usual he was lying down, his frayed blanket outlining his spindly limbs, his head right up against the tall chest. He was awake, his blank eyes unnerved me, but I counted on his silence. I stood on tiptoe right next to his face. He didn't flinch. If I stumbled, my heel would squash his nose. My ears glued to Aunt's shop and my eyes down at Uncle, I slid open the drawer above his head. Blood thumped like a piston in my ears.

If Kang-jin had kept his word, the letters would still be where I left them. He had. Leaving the purse where it was, only by feel, I twisted the clasp, took out a letter, shoved it into my pocket, and fast-stepped out to the outhouse, passing Aunt's shop, hoping that if she saw me, she'd think I was rushing to the outhouse.

I locked myself inside the outhouse and took out the letter; I wanted to make sure Mom's hasty handwriting was clear enough for Miss Go. I hoped Aunt wouldn't find out, at least not until tomorrow, when I would've handed it over to Miss Go. Then there would be no going back.

Chapter Twenty-Five

It was Sunday morning. In-sook and Mi-hae were already out. Aunt was putting on her makeup, getting ready for church. I was studying on our low table when someone banged on our door.

The incessant banging was followed by Yumi's excited voice, calling me. I ran out. She was breathless, she must have been running.

"Your mom . . . She's on the phone. She wants to talk! She's waiting!"

That made no sense. It had been only ten days since Miss Go wrote to Mom. From what Aunt said, letters took weeks or months to get to America. Yumi gave me her home phone number without asking her parents' permission. Neither of us ever thought my Mom would actually call. Overseas calls were prohibitively expensive, not many homes had the luxury of a telephone.

Yumi was bubbling over. Most likely, her family had never had a phone call from overseas, let alone from America. "Your mom wants to talk to your aunt. Quick." She yelled again.

"What, why my Aunt?" My heart fell. I frantically gestured at her to shush. Aunt mustn't hear what she said. But it was too late. Aunt was already at the door. She pushed me aside.

"What nonsense are you babbling about? What do you mean Su-young's mom's on the phone? What phone?"

Yumi, realising the damage she had caused, sheepishly repeated the message.

Aunt looked puzzled, then turned to me. "What have you done! Why is she calling me on their phone? What did you do behind my back, you . . ." She raised her hand to strike me.

"We have to go. She's waiting for you, Su-young-aunt. My mom is holding the phone. Please go quickly . . . it's from America, the cost of it all . . ."

Aunt clenched my wrist and headed up the road: "We follow you!"

Just like that we went off—Aunt with only half her makeup done, our shack door left wide open. Yumi was running ahead, glancing back with a horrified look on her face at Aunt dragging me by my wrist.

How long had I thought about connecting with Mom! But never this way. Not with furious Aunt next to me, listening to every word I'd say to Mom. I

238

somehow imagined Miss Go and Mom quietly working things out, away from Aunt's knowing, and then someday, I'd magically land in Mom's arms. Now I was more terrified than excited. After the phone call, Mom would still be thousands of miles away, while Aunt would drag me back home. The good news finally came, but wrapped in a deadly package.

It was the fastest and the slowest ten-minute walk ever to Yumi's house. When Yumi opened her gate, the dog barked ferociously. He lunged at Aunt, choking himself against the leash stretched to the limit. But Aunt was blind to him. She didn't notice the grandeur of Yumi's home either—the tall, handsome wooden gate, a spacious, cemented front yard, their many rooms, enough for each of Yumi's three sisters to have their own and housekeepers. Aunt homed directly into the room where Yumi pointed. She barely took her shoes off, rushed in and shut the door in my face. Yumi's mom came out, giving Aunt privacy. I could've done a hundred jumping jacks to hold down my adrenaline. Yumi grabbed my bobbing shoulders, trying to calm my pacing. But soon, both of us were pacing, holding hands. At one point, Yumi put her ear to the door but shook her head, she couldn't hear anything. I was too scared to go near it.

Then it began. Aunt's famous high-pitched staccato cursing shot through the door.

"You stupid, ungrateful bitch . . . how dare you, after all I've done for you!" Her shrilling penetrated through the door, stirring up the whole house. One by one, everyone came out; Yumi's mom, Yumi's two younger sisters, two maids from the kitchen. They all gathered in the yard, gaping at the door to Yumi's father's room where Aunt was. They had been politely staying out of the way but it was theatre now.

"You crazy fucking bitch, how dare you raise your voice at me! I god-dammed raised you . . . You're so quick to believe a stranger, and not me? Did you ever ask me how things were? Me? How dare you accuse me of mistreating her! She's the bastard you abandoned—yes, *you*, not me, you shit-head. I raised her far better than you ever could. Do you know how many times I went hungry so she didn't? And this's how you fucking repay me?"

Yumi's mom was aghast, stunned by Aunt's foul-mouthed abuse of her precious phone. Yumi's crazed dog howled and growled towards the door, his frenzied barking bounced off their cemented ground, shooting through the sky. The neighbourhood dogs heard the noise and joined in chorus. I was grateful that Yumi's father wasn't home. He'd have hung up the phone and thrown us out.

The whole forty-five extravagant minutes of their talk, their one and only talk in seven years, started and ended with one huge, ugly fight. Aunt could out-scream, out-curse, out-threaten the best of them, but never like this. I was even more impressed that Mom stayed on the phone, not giving in to Aunt's fury.

Despite this marathon fight, at the end of it, I still hoped to talk to Mom, even just to hear her voice.

Finally, Aunt came out, her face flushed and wild. Everyone spread out, giving her room. She had already hung up the phone. She didn't thank Yumi's mom, didn't even look at her. Instead, her eyes zoomed on me. She picked up her shoe, threw it at my head, and ran to me and slapped me. My head spun. She slapped me again. Their dog whimpered and went hiding in his kennel. And before anyone could say or do anything, she grabbed me by my hair and dragged me out of their house.

My scalp burned as her knuckles dug in deep. She was charging through the streets like a fiery ghoul. How could a woman as old as Aunt walk so fast? I kept stumbling, barely able to keep up under her grip. She scolded me all the way home: "Were you out of your mind? You come between me and my sister? Humiliate me in front of Yumi's family? How dare you! How dare you go behind my back! Telling her all those lies. Who knew I was raising a snake! What were you thinking with that pea brain of yours? You thought your mom's going to come running and get you? She can't! You're stuck with me. I send you to school to study and this is what you do to me? You deserve to die, you ungrateful half-witted bitch."

Only a few people were out and about on this Sunday morning, and no one gave a look or a thought to us. Parents had absolute power over their kids' discipline. What seemed like an 'angry mom catching her wayward daughter' scene would have drawn their sympathy to Aunt: "That young wretch deserved it."

When we got home, she shoved me into the room, locking the door from outside.

"Don't you move. Don't you dare try to sneak out. If you do, I *will* find you and break your skinny little neck!"

Hours passed. Aunt stayed away, forcing me to stew in uncertainty of the punishment to come. My imagination ran wild, itself a torture—better to be beaten and get it over with. But hour after hour, only more waiting waited. I comforted myself by saying, you made this happen, so see it through, it'll end sooner or later, she hasn't killed you, yet. Then my thoughts went darker. Why did she call for Aunt instead of me? Did she not believe what Miss Go wrote, did she not believe me? She knew Aunt's temper. By calling her didn't she know she was putting me in great danger? If only I'd had a chance to stop Yumi from talking before Aunt came out, what bad luck! Perhaps Mom really doesn't want me, then I'd be lost for good. I went over every bit of what little I'd heard of their phone fight and Aunt's ravings on the way home. I didn't see anything positive happening from that phone call.

How wonderful it would have been at least to hear her voice. I wondered if I'd even remember her voice. I remembered the emotion it brought me when she called me her little puppy or her little monkey, but I no longer could recall the timbre or the colour of her voice.

• • •

Night had fallen and it was dark outside our small window.

"What's this? Why's the door locked? What's going on? Anybody home?" In-sook was rattling the door, back from her academy, finally showing a sign of life.

"In-sook-ah, come in this way," Aunt shouted from her shop. Her door opened, then closed and all was silent again. If Aunt was telling In-sook about the phone call from America, she was whispering it. Practically next door, I couldn't hear anything.

Then Mi-hae came home too, also going directly to Aunt's shop. Now I heard their voices, especially Mi-hae's: "I knew she'd do something sneaky like this. I should've pushed her into that shit hole then. I hate that bitch. She should die for this, mom. Why aren't we doing anything! What're we waiting for?"

For all her outer beauty, Mi-hae's temperament and vocabulary matched Aunt's. Aunt quietened her.

Silence.

Dinnertime came but I didn't get any. I listened for their voices. Nothing.

Time to go to sleep. No one came into the room. How could that be? Even the cheapest inn was too expensive for us. Was keeping me locked up that important? I wouldn't know where to run that Aunt couldn't find me. Yumi's home was the only place, but I couldn't burden them, not after what happened there.

Uncle hadn't moved from his corner. Aunt had taken him out only once but with no other sleeping bodies near him, he seemed eerily more alive, as if he might rise up at any moment and shuffle over to me like a zombie.

All night, I was half awake, half asleep, fighting off killers, running through the frozen alleyways and hills that were the nightly settings of my dreams.

The next day, Monday, was a school day but Aunt didn't let me out of the locked room.

The first class, second class, lunch time; I followed the school day in my head. I thought of Yumi, what she might be thinking about, why I hadn't shown up. Aunt was restrained, distant. She didn't ask for my excuses. I didn't offer my apologies. I stayed docile as if being locked up was the normal thing, like taking a sick day from school. Aunt took away my daily chores— cleaning the urine bucket, fetching water, helping with cooking and washing. I wasn't allowed to go to the outhouse. She said to use the urine bucket, then emptied the bucket herself. She only came in the room to feed Uncle and to take him out, locking the shack behind her each time. Twice, she brought me a bowl of ramen noodles. They were absolutely delicious.

By the afternoon of the next day, my mind became

confused. I no longer knew what I was waiting for. The room began playing tricks on me: sometimes it seemed so small and stifling that I could barely breathe; other times, the room stretched out to the vast empty streets and beyond, and I became smaller and smaller, seeing myself like a dried-up worm on sun-burnt cement. I tried to think about singing and the music Miss Jung played for me, but my mind fell silent. I read words in my school books, but the words turned themselves into Mom's letters, the phone call, Yumi, her dog's barking, teachers, the chatter of my classmates. Eventually, even these images slowed and faded, then came to a complete stop, going back to just being words on the page, my mind as blank as Uncle's eyes.

On the third day, Aunt pushed in a bowl of rice and kimchee. If she'd given me a quick glance or put the rice bowl down a bit gentler, I would've been broken; I'd have begged for her forgiveness. But she didn't linger, shutting the door in that impersonal, cold way as she had done the previous two days.

I felt calmer that third day, my wandering mind coming to a complete rest. Listening for sounds didn't get me excited anymore, I slept, and when I woke up, I forced myself back to sleep. Then I heard a gentle voice asking if I wanted to come out, didn't I want some fresh air?

I opened my eyes. Kang-jin was staring down at me, his voice friendly, even concerned. With no other option than to follow him, I stumbled out. Fresh air and the harsh light cut me. We walked, Kang-jin leisurely, I guardedly. This wasn't a cousinly stroll. I realised that this was the first time we'd ever walked together. Actually I'd never seen him outside in the last ten years, except in the church, and even that was indoors. But then, Kang-jin didn't stroll with In-sook or Mi-hae either, even when they were younger— always a young man with a purpose.

Out of nowhere, he put his arm around me; he chuckled at my flinching and shook me gently: "Su-young-ah. Why so tense? Don't worry, everything's going to be fine. We're just going out for a dinner, we should've done this a long time ago. But here we are, never too late."

He glowed in a public place. From the corner of my eyes, I saw how confidently he moved, taking his jaunty steps in well-polished, expensive brown shoes. He couldn't afford them from his tutoring salary. From Jae-in, I thought. His finely cut pants looked recently ironed, going straight down to his shoes with a just-so light crease around the ankles. He held his body straight as in a military parade, but even that somehow seemed to add to his casual chic. Two high school girls in their uniforms walked toward us, faltering their steps and staring at Kang-jin with that awe-struck look. They pushed each other, giggling like ten-year-olds, their modesty busted in the presence of such a handsome vision. Kang-jin squeezed my shoulder, pulling me closer to him, as if to make them jealous.

He took me to a Chinese restaurant, more upscale than the takeout place I was used to. Since it was still too early for dinner, we had the whole place to ourselves. Kang-jin ordered black bean noodles for me. His suave manner made the waiter jump to it. Kang-jin asked if I wanted anything else, ordering for himself something elaborate I had not heard of.

A soft late afternoon sunlight streamed in from the window adding to the drama of our setting. An outdated, sad love song floated in from a radio. Kang-jin lit a cigarette with a flick of his fingers and inhaled. As he exhaled, leisurely smoke billowed from his mouth, then he inhaled it a second time through his nostrils. Sitting on the high-backed black lacquered chair, he looked movie-star handsome, poised, confident, even romantic.

The food came. As hungry as I was, I couldn't enjoy it. When the dishes were cleared, he took up another cigarette.

"Su-young-ah, we've a special relationship, you and I. You know that, don't you? And you know how fond I am of you." He spoke in a low, oily voice, looking at me meaningfully, pointedly.

I knew no such thing. Only unspeakable, vile things existed between us. I fidgeted in my seat, unsure of where his talk was going.

"See? You feel it too. We needn't have secrets

between us. You can trust me . . . I'll take care of you . . . Aunt didn't beat you up, did she? I told her not to."

I never understood his talk. That day of his attack and now, his words ran in a circle that he drew around himself, talking as if what he was saying were facts, important for both him and me.

"Why didn't you tell me about writing to your mom? I gave you my trust, and you betrayed that. That makes me sad. I could've helped you if that was what you wanted, made it easier for you, for all of us. Instead you embarrassed and hurt your aunt."

I listened and thought. It was more likely that he and Aunt were simply buying time to figure out what to do with me, just like I had to figure out what to do. After all, they couldn't keep me locked up forever. I hated Kang-jin. The word, hate, was not strong enough, too diluted, too inept to express what I felt. I hated him so intensely that I imagined attacking him right where he sat, with the dirty chopsticks, one in each eye. Instead, I just sat helpless with that ever-present fear I felt whenever I was with him. Still, seeing him in person was less frightening than seeing him in my head. And here in this public place, I felt safe.

"I know you are having a tough time at school. I'm going to get you the tuition, so you can finish your middle school. And I'll take care of your high school and university too. If you're behind in school, I'll tutor you." Even to him, his words must have rung false, he changed his tone. "You can go back to school tomorrow.

But *do not* linger on. Come home after school right away. Understood? Don't cross me again . . ." and he got up, dismissing me. Now that was more like the Kang-jin I knew and understood.

Walking back home, I felt uneasy, it was all too simple, getting off free with a mere three days of being locked up, ending with a fancy meal. I knew there had to be more, but what?

As Kang-jin promised, Aunt let me go back to school the following day, with my much-delayed tuition fees in my hand.

Chapter Twenty-Six

Yumi was ecstatic, she kept punching my shoulders with her tomboy fists, so relieved after my three days of silence. She'd been worried sick so despite her mom's objection, she came by the shack looking for me, but Aunt came out instead. I was out with Kang-jin for that strange dinner. Yumi rolled her eyes heavenward and gave her theatrical head shake: "Wow, your aunt. Really scary. She cursed at me and accused me of causing trouble, said if I didn't scram, she'd throw me a bucket of salt, that I was evil, a bad influence, and that I should never come near you again. Can you believe it? I ran away as fast as I could." Aunt did sometimes throw salt at people as the final insult when her cursing wasn't enough.

Yesterday when I got home after my dinner with Kang-jin, Aunt was waiting in her shop. We talked or rather, she talked.

"Su-young-ah, tell me truthfully. Whose idea was it? I don't believe you'd go behind my back and write to your mom. You're not like that. It was Yumi and that fat cow, her mom, wasn't it? They coaxed you into doing it, didn't they?"

I didn't answer her. I could've said no, but I was sure she knew it was me; she was simply trying to save our faces, so we could go on. Aunt decided to blame the whole thing on innocent Yumi and her mom. It was true that Yumi's mom was on the plump side but calling her a fat cow was a jealous slur: not many could afford fat around their bellies. Korea was still a poor country.

"What could they possibly know about us? What gives them the right to meddle in our family? I could sue them! Well, what's done is done, I'm sorry I've been neglectful. It's all my fault. But you know I'm doing my best. I didn't know how unhappy you've been." This was a very different Aunt than the Aunt of the last three days. Still, she had changed much over the years; thinner, more frazzled, constantly looking for money. Education was the only way out of our poverty. Aunt had done and would do anything to educate her children. Unfortunately, her arms just didn't reach all the way to me.

"Su-young-ah, let's forget what happened and start over. I'll be more sensitive to your needs. And about your mom, the money she sent me for you to go to America, what a joke—she thought that puny sum would be enough to get you there! It wouldn't even cover your airline ticket. What about all the other costs? What about your immigration papers? What about your passport? What about all the work I've done taking care of you? What do I get? Things cost a lot more now than seven years ago. I'm telling you— when she's not crazy, she's just stupid, never could think things through. But I promise you, if I ever get a letter from her, you'll be the first one to read it. Okay? Do we agree? Are we good?"

I nodded in agreement, and I let her go on and on about Mom. No sane person would contradict Aunt. But I'd been working on a plan of my own. If Mom couldn't send for me, I would run away to become a nun—a nun like Hildegard von Bingen, an abbess in twelfth-century Germany. Miss Jung told us about her one day during choir practice. None of my choir members were interested in hearing about some nun from medieval times. But she made an impression on me. Hildegard von Bingen dedicated her life to the arts, as a composer, writer and philosopher. If there were nuns like her that long ago, then I could be one now. Or be like Miss Jung! I could easily imagine being her—both a musician and a nun who travelled to foreign lands helping others. I planned to find her. Even if she was in a jungle in Vietnam, her church would know where to send my letter.

Whether I became a nun or not, at least for now, I was happy looking at the familiar faces of my classmates. Yumi and I ran down to the small shop in the school. It sold books, pencils, notebooks, art supplies, gym clothes, and packed lunches, snacks and soft drinks. We splashed out and brought back an armful of food for lunch. Besides my tuition, Aunt also had given me money enough for lunch and bus fare.

"Is Kim Su-young here?" A student from another class stuck her head in, "Miss Go wants to see her." I ran down to the teacher's hall. I was going to see her as soon as I'd finished lunch to tell her about Mom's phone call.

When I got to the teacher's hall, I found her talking to a man. He was leaning against her desk, smoking a cigarette. He didn't look like a teacher or a parent. She signalled me to come over. Normally reserved Miss Go was all aflutter, barely able to contain her excitement.

"Su-young-ah, this is Mr. Park, a private agent your mom sent. He's going to work on your immigration case and get you to America!"

I didn't think I heard her right. What was she talking about? What agent?

Miss Go repeated, "Su-young-ah. Your mom is going to get you to America. Mr. Park here is going to help you, he knows what to do. Now he needs to talk with you." Then she handed me a leave-permission slip. "Go with him now."

Dazed, I followed the man out.

In the corridor, he asked if there was a coffee bar nearby. I told him of one.

"I'll wait for you there. Stay in school for a bit, then meet me in fifteen minutes or so. But don't tell anyone about me or where you're going," and he was gone.

I didn't know what to think. I wanted to go back to Miss Go for more explanation but feared I might ruin something, though I didn't know what I would ruin. So I waited ten minutes, then walked out of the school and went to the coffee bar.

The coffee bars around our school were like speakeasies for students. They were not illegal, but teachers frowned on them. Parents discouraged our using them, too, calling them a waste of precious study time. They also felt this new coffee craze from America was bad for young bodies. But we were impatient. We wanted to be grown up already and do grown up things. So we went to the coffee bars whenever we could, right after school or in between evening academies. They were an oasis from the endless study rounds. We could relax, away from watchful grown ups, feeling like adults ourselves, at least while we sipped our coffee under the soft lighting, listening to music. The Spanish classical guitarist, Antonio Segovia, was very popular among high school and university students and often played, so we, middle schoolers, had to listen to him too. Pithy sayings from popular Western poems decorated the walls. Edgar Allan Poe was much admired. We memorised his poems in English to keep their original, beautiful rhythms. Especially his *Annabel Lee*. Even I, the worst of the students, memorised it and could recite it in English. The coffee bar was the hip place to be seen. I enjoyed it whenever Yumi invited me, but not often—I hated being on the receiving end of her kindness all the time.

Still in the middle of the school afternoon, the coffee bar was empty. Mr Park sat alone in a dark corner, smoking. But even if it had been crowded, I'd have easily recognised his big mop of curly hair, like he was wearing a helmet indoors. Most Koreans had straight hair except women who permed theirs as a fashion statement. So he stood out. We had a saying that curly haired people had wickedly bad tempers. I wondered who'd win if he and Aunt got into a fight. Aunt didn't have curly hair.

"Your mom sent me to get you out. And that's what I'm here to do," he announced as soon as I sat down. "For the next couple of weeks, I am going to take you to places to process your immigration. Miss Go will give you the leave slip. We'll meet in this shop and go from there. We'll try to get everything done during your school hours, and we'll do it quietly and quickly. So here's the most important thing you must do for me: Don't tell anyone what you're doing with me. When you get home, act normally. Don't mention me, you don't know me, no one talked to you about me or your mom. And don't tell your friends either. We don't want your aunt finding out. It'll make my job difficult, not to mention yours. Understood?"

All I could do was nod. I didn't want to jinx any of it with questions. I couldn't have made this up, even in a dream.

"We start tomorrow. What time does the school open?"

I told him at eight in the morning.

"Okay. Be on time to school tomorrow. Go to your first class. Then come here at nine. When we are done, you go back to school, finish the remainder of the classes, then go home as if you'd been in school all day, got it?" He picked up his cigarette pack and left, giving me no time to digest or ask questions. I had many.

I went back to school in the middle of maths class, but Mr. Bae didn't yell at me. Miss Go must have already told him about Mr. Park. The rest of my school day was a waste. My body sat in the classroom, but my mind was a ping-pong ball bouncing from wall to wall. The last three days had been unreal, from the letter to Mom, the phone call, and now, Mr. Park. Mom really knew how to surprise me. But how does one prepare for such a sudden change in life? I walked home thinking, "Until you get to America, don't get hurt, don't get sick, don't walk under the ladders, that's bad luck, avoid asphalt cracks, also bad luck." How quickly things changed. Life suddenly became very precious.

"What're you thinking about so hard?"

I looked up, startled. The last person I expected to

see. Kang-jin was standing by Aunt's shop door, smoking. He never came home two days in a row, but here he was. He grabbed my schoolbag, "Come in this way." He stepped aside to let me into the shop, following me in, closing the door behind him. Aunt was not in, but a plate of half-eaten sweet melon sat on her worktable. She couldn't be far away, then. Kang-jin sat on the work stool.

"How was school? Was it good to go back?" he asked, in a friendly way.

I kept my head down, afraid that he might see from my eyes the incredible day I had, and my secret, Mr. Park.

"May I see your schoolbag?" he said. Without waiting for my answer, he unbuckled my schoolbag, turned it upside down, and shook its contents loose; the pencil box clanged open, pencils, erasers rolling out onto the floor, my books and notebooks fell out too. Kang-jin examined the inside of my empty schoolbag, feeling for lumps and around its edges. He then picked up my books and notebooks, one at a time, leafed through, glancing at my handwritten notes.

"Come here," he said, "closer." He stuck his hands in my uniform pockets. Nothing was inside. He felt up my chest, around my waist and patted my skirt all around.

"Did anything unusual happen today? At school? Anyone talk to you?"

I shook my head, no.

Done with his detective work, he said, "You can go in. But remember what I said yesterday. You come to me first if you need anything."

That was the first day of my living a double life.

Chapter Twenty-Seven

With everyone cooped up in class, the street was deserted. In this quiet morning lull, the sound of my footsteps on the concrete bounced off loudly, echoing as if I was walking through a tunnel. I kept looking around as I walked along the tall stone wall that ran the length of the school, listening for other footsteps, someone following me, perhaps, even Kang-jin, in his creepy way.

The coffee bar was at the end of the street, around the corner, facing the busy main boulevard. Mr. Park was leaning on the door frame, smoking. The coffee bar was closed, still too early in the day. He gave me a quick nod, then putting out the cigarette, shuffled ahead. I walked a few paces behind. He hailed a taxi at the next corner and hopped in, leaving the door open for me.

For the next two weeks, Mr. Park took me to places in Seoul I'd never been, sometimes the same place twice in a day. I worried someone might recognise me and tell Aunt or Kang-jin. I was especially anxious when we went to the hospital for my physical checkup. For all I knew, we could've been in Kang-jin's fiancée's hospital. What if I ran into her or if she was the one to examine me? We met only once, I remembered her well but I counted on her not remembering me. I was not memorable. And thanks to Uncle, my last name was not Woo but Kim.

A doctor measured and prodded every part of my body like livestock up for auction. He also shot me full of vaccines.

We went to a photo studio for my immigration papers and passport. Since Mom left, the only pictures I had of me were in my classroom group photos, once at the beginning of the school year and once during the school picnic where we paid for a copy. So this private photo session was meaningful—as the photographer took great care working his tall standing camera, the lights and my stance—like declaring, "I am real, I exist."

At the immigration office, a mob of people, unwilling to form lines, shoved and elbowed one another for a minute advantage. Mr. Park never looked frustrated, guarding his stacks of paper, and seemed to have all the time in the world, just doing part of his job he knew well. With infinite patience, he waited everywhere we went, waiting for the papers to be stamped, waiting to submit the papers. On these long days, he took me to lunch at simple little places wherever we happened to be. Then uncharacteristically, he'd get motherly, pushing dishes towards me, gesturing for me to eat and eat. It was a startling contrast from his gruff personality.

Mr. Park didn't talk or smile much except once. We were waiting in line at the immigration office where he seemed to have run into a friend. In a matter of seconds, he became a different person. His face lit up, thoroughly delighted, and like Yumi often did, he kept hitting his friend's shoulder, so hard that I thought the man might keel over. Then something made them laugh; Mr. Park's large helmet head rolled back and a big woofing sound roared from the back of his throat, his whole body shaking in genuine joy. It was so infectious I laughed along for no reason.

He did one thing that especially endeared me to him. He made sure I got on the bus back to school no matter how long the wait. I felt awkward and even uncomfortable having him wait around with me. No one had shown me this kind of consideration before.

It was at the American embassy that I finally felt the full impact of what we'd been doing for the past two weeks. The embassy was an impressive building with a soaring stone facade, sleek floors and high ceilings. Inside, once again I saw Americans and for the first time, black soldiers with their sparkling dark eyes. Americans had that unique amiable, pleasant gait.

Koreans didn't smile at strangers; Americans looked directly at you with the big, uncomplicated smiles that said: "I am happy to see a fellow human being."

Coming out of the embassy, I felt a real hope, like someone had bundled up my last seven years, took them away, and in its place, handed me a pass to America. I finally allowed myself to imagine flying away.

At the end of the second week, while we were waiting for my bus back to school, Mr. Park handed me an envelope. "Here. Your mom wanted you to have this. Do what you want with it. Eat, I say. Put some meat on your bones. Grow."

Inside was a neat stack of money. I stared at it, my mind flying off . . . all the food I could eat, buses I could take everyday, even invite Yumi to the coffee bar. "Put that in your bag before someone sees it," he warned.

On the bus, I kept feeling for the envelope of money. I felt Mom's warmth. I felt freer and more grounded, too. I had one dilemma. I didn't know where to hide it. I couldn't bring it home. If Aunt found out, not just this money, but also my future would be gone in one breath. Despite her new kindness, Aunt was still watchful. I couldn't ask Yumi to keep it for me, she'd ask questions. Hiding it in my school desk was unsafe; we never sat at the same desk day after day. When we cleaned the classroom, we stacked up all the desks to one side, swept and mopped the floor, and did the same on the other side. Desks got mixed up. And so I worried about where to put my money, but it was a fun worry to have.

A few days later when I got home, Kang-jin was visiting yet again, talking with Aunt. I quickly turned and walked away, but he had already seen me. He hollered at me to come back. We stood by the kitchen cupboard; Aunt was in her shop, just a few steps away, with only a curtain separating her and us. I could hear her scissors snipping away at a fabric. I felt safer. He inspected my schoolbag again but less thoroughly this time. But he probed my body more thoroughly, the narrow and dark kitchen space giving him the cover, all the while asking me the same stupid questions: did I see anyone new, did anyone approach me at school? And saying I should always come to him first.

I denied it all, standing there, gritting my teeth as his spidery fingers crawled up and down inside my uniform. He'd never find my money. It was safe, wrapped in plastic and a piece of newspaper, behind the chicken coop at the landlord's, where there was a small wasteland of junk—piles of loose rocks, mounds of chicken poop and rotting straws. It turned out to be the safest place, where no one lingered.

Kang-jin's fingers continued their probing. But I realised I didn't have to take this with Aunt in the next room. Even for her, this scene had to be crazy. I felt emboldened; I leaned on the kitchen cupboard and gave a quick push. The cupboard, supported only by thin wooden legs, wobbled, lost its balance; the bowls, pots, frying pan, and utensils all tumbled down, and fell on Kang-jin, startling him. A knife fell point first and punctured the instep of his right foot. He screamed and Aunt rushed in. The cut was small but deep, blood trickling out. Aunt rushed him into her shop to treat him. I felt a rush of satisfaction. Finally for once, I'd got the upper hand. I pushed the wobbly cupboard back upright but it wouldn't stand. It would need braces to secure the legs. I patted it, thanking it, as I lined the dented pots, pans and bowls on the ground. Made of aluminum, the pots dented easily but rarely broke.

That was the last time Kang-jin came home to inspect me. Aunt continued to be kind. In-sook and Mi-hae never mentioned Aunt's phone call with Mom, or my three day lock-up. I wondered if Aunt and Mom had written to each other since. I decided not to check her purse for new letters, it was no longer important.

Chapter Twenty-Eight

"Ah, there she is. What perfect timing! Su-young-ah, come on in. We were just talking about you. Come, bow to our guest," said Aunt.

A large, matronly woman had been chatting with Aunt, fanning herself.

"Sit. Sit here." Aunt patted the floor next to her.

I stole a glance at the visitor while sitting down. Our eyes met. Under the woman's hooded eyelids, a pair of small, cruel eyes peered out, looking me up and down very thoroughly. Her pudgy face was pasty white in heavy makeup, punctuated by painted blood-red lipsticks and thick black arched brows. Her multiple chins rested on her massive breasts which lolled on to her bulging stomach. Our tiny room encased her like a cage. Just by the act of sitting, the woman looked uncomfortably hot; a sleek layer of sweat covered her face. She fanned it vigorously.

"This is my niece, Su-young. As I told you, she sings beautifully. She can mimic any singer, after hearing them just once. She sings solos at her school and at her church." Aunt emphasised "church" as if it added a special value.

The woman nodded, her eyes still gauging me. She commented: "She's small."

"Yes, she's small for her age but she'll grow," Aunt said, adding, "But why would you want big? Nothing big ever tasted good. Small is better."

I looked at Aunt in disbelief. She winked at me through her glasses: "We'll talk later, Su-young-ah. All's going to be wonderful."

"Why don't you sing something for me now?" the woman croaked.

Aunt glanced at me looking at her with disbelief. She quickly said, "Let's wait for another time. I'll need to talk to Su-young first."

"Well, then," the woman hit her thigh with her folded fan once, marking the end of the meeting. "We'll talk again next week then, after you've talked to her," she said pointing her fan at me.

She lumbered up with difficulty, trying to balance on her legs to support her massive upper body. She waddled out, leaving behind her a trail of thick, repulsive scent. Aunt chased after her and whispered something at the door.

Aunt came back, all smiles—warm, specific, dangerous smiles.

"Su-young-ah. Let's talk," she said, sitting across from me. "You've been with me since you were five. I raised all of you the same . . . I love you all equally, you, In-sook, Mi-hae, Kang-jin . . ."

Every time she started this way, I worried. Nothing good ever followed that sentence.

"You know how hard things have become at home. Kang-jin helps out from what little he makes tutoring. But he's still in school. And we can't rely on his fiancée, they are not married yet. Since you broke us up, me and your mom, she hasn't written, hasn't sent money. And how dumb is your mom, I ask you. Spending all that money on a phone call, just to fight with me so that she can vent her misery, embarrassing me in front of everyone. She could've sent that money to me instead, to help us . . . What did that phone call get us? Nothing. Zero. Did I force her to leave you with me? It was her choice. So she can't blame me for our lives turning out badly. I didn't plan this. Listen. As far as you are concerned, I'm your family. It's time to forget your mom. Let her go. Let her live hers and let us live ours in our way. I'll take care of you as I always have. I'll never abandon you."

"Believe me, I've thought long and hard, done everything I could, but I can't do anymore. I can't afford to send all of you to school, not all at once," Aunt's voice quivered, her frustration genuine.

"Mi-hae can't quit her university with only one more year to go. If she quit now, that'd be the end of her chances of ever getting a decent job or a good husband. And In-sook, you see how hard she studies. Day and night, that's all she does. Kang-jin says she's good enough to try for Seoul University. How can we deprive her of that? Once In-sook gets out of university, she'll have a job of her choice and pull her weight to help the family. So . . . you help now. I am asking very little from you. You don't have to sacrifice anything. Your life won't change at all."

So I wasn't getting off that easy after Mom's phone call.

"The woman you met, Madame Daisy," she pronounced her "Dae-ji," which sounded just like "pig" in Korean. (Aunt couldn't shape a diphthong.) It was a perfect name for Madame Daisy. It matched the way she looked. "She's from the next door—she's very interested in you. She says she'll pay for your education, even for college. All she asks in return is that you sing at her place a few nights a week. You'll still go to school and your church and continue to do exactly as you've been doing. It's not asking much, besides you love singing. She knows some important clients who can help you get ahead with your singing. How wonderful is that? Kang-jin says it's a great idea too, that you're born to sing. This could be the quickest way to your singing career."

I sat dumbfounded. So, this was their grand plan. To sell me to the brothel. Pleased at my lack of protest, Aunt's words gushed out more.

"It's easy. Right next door. You go to school during the day, at night you just hop over, sing a little, you hop right back, eat and sleep at home. How simple is that! Finally, all that singing will pay off, supporting the family for once."

A few days ago coming home from school, I'd seen Aunt rushing out of the whorehouse and sliding back into her shop. I thought she went there to complain about their late-night noises or give them what for about their customers peeing and even pooping between their door and our wall. But she hadn't looked angry; she was talking about me, about turning me into one of them.

Unfortunately, after two weeks of clandestine outings, Mr. Park disappeared from sight, without telling me what to plan or to think. The last thing he had said was that his job was done, and now we must wait for the officials to do their part. Weeks went by without Miss Go handing me the leave slip. And the weeks became a month and then another month. It was as if I had made it all up in my head. I couldn't badger Miss Go about Mr. Park. One didn't just burst into the teacher's hall or stop her in the hallway demanding to know, "What's next?"

I didn't even know Mr. Park's full name or in which agency he worked. Kids didn't ask a grown up for his business card or credentials. He didn't chit chat with me when we'd waited in those long queues or at the bus stops. He kept to himself, lighting one cigarette after another. I couldn't name the hospital, the photo studio, or the location of the immigration office. The truth was, part of me wanted it that way: the less I knew, the less it meant, the less real. I'd been happy simply to follow him along. Even when I gathered enough courage to hope, I still kept some doubt, just in case, for a softer falling—treating it like a diversion, like coming up empty handed after scratching on a lottery ticket, or like "easy come easy go," as Aunt would say. It was, after all, such a preposterous idea. Now Madame Daisy had joined the gang, closing in on me.

I lay awake listening to the fitful chatter of passers by, the nightly music of someone peeing on our wall, a vendor calling out for last-minute munchies, making that distinct sound of clacking wooden blocks, a police officer whistling the final warning of curfew, chasing away the many drunken businessmen every night, then the eventual deathly silence.

The morning folded the night. I'd been awake since the curfew.

Chapter Twenty-Nine

"Hey, you. Su-young. Student. Hey!" The woman screeched into the street.

I walked faster. Surely she could see I was rushing to school. Unfazed, she shouted louder, "Su-young-ah. Stop right there!" Pedestrians stopped, staring at me, at her. A hot flush ran through my face. She wasn't someone you wanted to be seen with or talking to. But I quickly turned and gave a short bow before she made things worse.

Madame Daisy, as enormous as a sumo wrestler, stood in front of her whorehouse, her garish wrinkled dress riding up above the fat rolls of her knees, the last night's makeup still stuck in the crevices of her wrinkles, her mouth one big red circle of smeared lipstick. She must have just got up, or was about to go to bed.

Madame wanted to know when I was going to show off my singing; why don't I come and sing for her clients one night, how about this week. Her flabby arm leaned against the door frame, her other hand scratching the generous mound of her stomach. She moved her wide hips from side to side, in tune with some melody inside her head. She grinned, holding my gaze, waiting, enjoying my embarrassment.

I mumbled I didn't know . . . I'd ask Aunt about it . . . and that I was late for school. I bowed again and took off before she could say another word, but say, she did.

"Tell your aunt I want to talk to her! Soon . . ." she shouted after me.

I ran quickly down the hill and banged on the side of the bus that was about to set off. When the bus sped away, with me in it, I felt calmer.

Today, no matter what, I would ask Miss Go for Mr. Park's whereabouts. If I told her about Madame Daisy, she'd understand. But as soon as she walked in for the roll call, she signalled me over, and in front of everyone, said Mr. Park was waiting at the school gate, and that I should go to him right away.

Ignoring Yumi's questioning look, I rushed out, thinking, where was Miss Go's caution? And Mr. Park too. He should be waiting a block away, not at the school gate!

Leaning against the iron grill fence, Mr. Park was smoking as usual, gazing up at the drifting clouds. So overcome with joy, I ran to him, crying out, "Ahjussi!"— an all-purpose polite form of addressing an older man. I'd never addressed him before, not by any name. But then, he never called me by name either. Those niceties were not necessary. It had been over nine weeks since we last saw each other. He was real, after all; his expression same as before—unreadable. He nodded at me and got into the first taxi he saw.

We arrived at a very modern, grand hotel in Myung-Dong. He sauntered through the tall glass door that magically opened even before he pushed it. The cavernous lobby was serene and welcoming, made warm by the ambient lighting that studded the impossibly high ceiling like dimming stars. And from it, an enormous ball of lights hung down, suspended by a single rope. Mr. Park walked right under it. I circled around it. I counted more uniformed staff than customers. He continued on towards the back of the lobby where a box the size of a telephone booth opened up from the wall. He went in, held the door for me. An elevator! I'd only heard of them. I did my best to look casual. We rode up to the top floor, into a large restaurant. As soon as we sat down, a waiter came over, filled our glasses with yellow juice and gave Mr. Park a pot of coffee. The juice made my mouth water from its tart acidity—orange juice. I remembered its unique taste from the hard candies Mom brought.

Mr. Park said, "Let's eat. I'm starved."

Against the dark wood-panelled wall, a long white-clothed table stretched from one end to the other, displaying a multitude of sumptuous dishes, each dish a piece of artwork. Who'd dare to mess up such perfection? I'd never seen so much food in a single setting, not even on a New Year's Day. Tall white-hatted men stood behind each section, serving anyone who came near their stations. Mr. Park handed me a large plate and moved ahead, piling up food on his plate and mine.

After the unexpected feast, Mr. Park tapped out a cigarette. "Are you ready to go?" he asked. I was. But instead of getting up, he pushed an envelope toward me. As was his way, he hadn't said a word all through the meal.

"Here, your immigration has been approved. A week from today you'll be on the plane to your mom."

He pushed towards me the passport and airline ticket, Su-young Kim written on both.

"It'll be a long flight. America is a huge country. If our country is the size of the tip of my little finger, then America is my palm. You have to change planes in San Francisco, but the airport staff will take care of you. They will know you are a minor travelling alone from the badge you will wear. Always wear that, it'll help you get through your journey. Your family will be waiting for you at Dulles Airport in Washington, D.C."

I was bewildered. How could it be so easy? He went on, as if he heard my thoughts.

"With your mom already being an American, your case was simple and fast. The whole thing took less than three months!" he said, seemingly proud of his work.

"Your mom wanted to get you out as soon as possible. Next Thursday is the earliest we could do. The immigration office will be sending the notice to your aunt, but don't worry about that. It normally takes weeks to arrive. Your case was done so fast, it might get there sooner. Still by the time your aunt gets the notice, you'll be long gone. And even if she gets the notice tomorrow, it'll be too late for her to do anything, not against the government. She can't hold you here against your will."

Embarrassed by my tears, he reached for another cigarette. I excused myself to go to the bathroom.

Inside the restroom, I hollered, a loud silent holler. I paced the length of the restroom hall back and forth. I jumped about, banging on the countertop; I wanted the reality of my leaving to sink in; it was really happening. An elegantly dressed woman came out from one of the doors that lined the side of the restroom. She gave me a mean look for behaving like a savage in a public place.

"I'm going to America!" I offered as an excuse. How could I not say it? Like in the fable, she was the donkey into whose ears I had to tell this incredible news. She didn't think much of it. She huffed out. Then I saw how clean and large the restroom was. Red roses burst out from a vase in the middle of the row of sinks. A plush wide chair two people could fit in rested against the wall of mirrors. The tissue paper, soft as silk, bloomed out from a dainty little box. I opened the door from which the woman had emerged. Inside there was a spotless white toilet bowl, no stain anywhere. I sniffed. No smell. Incredible. Everything about this hotel felt like what was to come—America. At that moment, I promised myself that when I grew up, I'd have a bathroom just like this, so clean that if I wanted to, I could have a dinner party on the bathroom floor. Right then, my head jumped ahead: this bathroom to our outhouse, our shack, Aunt, her fury, the image of her dragging me to the whorehouse . . . could I really survive a whole week without her finding out? Mr. Park never met my Aunt. He had no idea what she was capable of. If she could steal money from her own church and her own sister, it'd be nothing to her to stop me, government or not. And what about my airline ticket and passport? What do I do with them until I leave? I didn't want them out of my sight. Could I leave them with Mr. Park? But what if something happened to him from now until next Thursday, like suffering an accident?

The anxiety and fear pounded me. I ran the cold water in the sink and plunged my face into it, then my entire head, staying in as long as I could. When I came up, from the mirror, I saw two eyes peeping through a wet, black mop. I'd never taken a serious look at myself before. No one looked at me the way they looked at Mi-hae. I thought my best part was my ears, they had nice curves and were well proportioned. In-sook once told me I was pretty when I sang. I decided what I had was an everyday face. Still the reality of me felt unreal. I was sorry for the girl in the mirror, for all that she'd been through, but she'd remained proud. For despite all, here she was, still standing, looking back at me.

I got back to the table and grudgingly asked Mr. Park to hold on to my ticket and passport till next Thursday.

"You're thinking ahead, kid. I wasn't going to give them to you anyway. My job's not done till I see you get on that plane. I'll meet you at the airport next Thursday. I'll then give you your mom's contact number too, just in case."

With great trepidation, I parted from Mr. Park and my getaway ticket.

"Don't worry about anything. Just make sure you show up at the airport. You're going to America," he said as I walked up to the bus. All the way back to school, his words circled round and round in my head, and soon I was chanting, "I'm going to America! I'm going to America!"

I floated into the classroom, certain that everyone would see my radiant glow. No one looked up, except Yumi who gave me the "where have you been!" look. Sitting among my classmates, it dawned on me that I was done here. I could literally walk out and no one could stop or punish me; no more hiding, no more embarrassment. In America, I'd have no history attached to me. I could set my timer to zero and begin again.

At lunch, I went to see Miss Go. Words failed me so I kept bowing to her, only repeating, thank you, over and over. She was very pleased at the outcome of her help. After school, Yumi and I walked the long way home, holding hands. It felt great to unload my last three months of adventure. She promised me she'd keep it a secret till I left; we didn't want Aunt to get a whiff of it. Still I knew she wouldn't be able to resist telling her mom and her sisters. Sudden sadness overwhelmed us. We held each other and cried.

• • •

Standing across the street from our shack, I prayed for a quiet, boring home for the next seven days. Then come next Thursday, I'd leave for school like any other day, but I'd go to the airport instead, meet Mr. Park, and get on that plane. Eventually Aunt might go looking for me at school or at Yumi's. Or, even sweeter, she'd be holding a notice saying that I'd flown away to America.

But as soon as I crossed the street, I heard Aunt yelling. Interestingly, she wasn't yelling at my cousins or a customer, but at a woman I had never seen before. The woman knelt in front of Aunt, her head on the floor, taking Aunt's verbal abuse without resistance. She kept calling Aunt "mother" in a strange bleating way that grated on my ears.

"Don't you call me mother!" Aunt screeched. "How dare you call me that! Why am I your mother?" Overcome with her anger, she kicked at the woman's head and shoulders, spewing out a string of obscenities. In-sook and Mi-hae pulled Aunt back. Aunt sobbed, pounding her chest, lamenting her bad fortune. In-sook and Mi-hae looked on, speechless.

She was a woman of indeterminate age, she could have been my age, fifteen, or thirty. Listening to her made it obvious she wasn't educated. Her vocabulary was limited, laced with a snail-paced southern accent, making her seem slower in the head than she probably was. She was farmers' stock through and through: from the shoulders to her hips, nothing curved in or out, her body and thick arms and legs imitating a tree trunk and its branches. Her round pink face reminded me of Lee. All through Aunt's beating, the woman didn't move, only covering her stomach. She kept repeating, "I am sorry, mum … forgive me, mum." The woman muttered that she'd take anything coming to her, until Aunt forgave her and accepted her and the baby inside. Aunt screamed again at the mention of the baby and lunged at her; In-sook held her back; Aunt fell backward, banging into Uncle behind her. In-sook and Mi-hae helped her up. I went out and brought some water for Aunt.

"Look here, whoever you are. The last thing I need is you and that thing you think you have," said Aunt. Then taking a reasoned approach she said, "You came to the wrong place, I'm telling you. We've nothing to do with you or it." Aunt flicked her wrist at our room: "Can't you see how poor we are? Why on earth would you want to come into this rat's ass of a place?"

The young woman sheepishly said that even she was surprised, but she knew poverty well, and our shack was far better than going back to her family down south where her father would kill her for sure, showing up in her condition. Brazenly, she added that Kang-jin will be getting a good job soon, and then we'll all live together in a big house . . . he's a smart man, isn't he, that man of hers . . . At that, Aunt completely lost control. She looked around, grabbed the wooden pillow from under Uncle's head, and threw it at the woman. She didn't flinch, the wooden pillow bouncing off her shoulder.

"How dare you speak my son's name from that filthy hole of yours! I know my Kang-jin. He'd never do such a thing. Why, he has a princess for a fiancée. You're no better than that piss bucket out there. And even if you trapped him into this disgusting horror show, how do we know it's his child. I can smell a scheming bitch miles away!"

But no matter what Aunt said, the woman wasn't moved, she insisted that she was marrying Kang-jin. She'd known no other men before him.

"He can't possibly love you! Look at you!" Aunt exclaimed. The frumpy hair tied back and the ill-fitting dress down to her threadbare ankle socks screamed a factory worker or restaurant help. The woman replied she didn't know anything about love, only that what

Kang-jin did to her was a sign he wanted to marry her. Then she stunned us with the next revelation. When asked how they met, she said she was the housekeeper at Kang-jin's tutoring home where they both lived, Jae-In's uncle's place. That meant Jae-in's uncle might already know about the affair, and Jae-in, too.

Aunt's eyes bulged and she struggled for words but only managed "Ah . . . ah . . . ah."

Then, the woman stretched out from her turtle-shell posture and sat up straight. She smoothed her hair and dress, and spoke in her unique, slow speech: "He come home drunk, I take care him. I, tiger." On the word 'tiger' she poked her finger in her chest. "I protect him. Nobody find out," she said with pride, "I wash Kang-jin things. He study late, I put food in him. Me, his chopstick. When he tired, I make him good. I take care. I know." Then she dropped the final bombshell: "You don't want me your daughter, I go. I go police place. I tell rape." Satisfied with that delivery, she gave a kind of snort and patted her stomach with a fat, coarse hand.

She might have looked like Lee but she was not like her. Lee had laughing Buddha eyes, this woman had steel in hers. When she spoke, she used her slow broken speech to her advantage, emphasising a word one way, pausing another. She took command of the room, and held us spellbound.

Aunt collapsed. We rushed over, helped her to lie down. Silence fell. Aunt had betrayed her church, husband, sister, and niece, only to come to this. And the one person who could console or counsel her, Kang-jin, had caused it all. Mi-hae, thoroughly disgusted, stormed out, swore she was done with the family. In-sook genuinely cared, but she was only sixteen, without wisdom or solution.

Aunt, who never got sick, not even a cold, fell seriously ill. It was unnerving to see her pale and broken. We didn't realise what a central role she played in our lives. She was our general. We got her cues for every move we made. Everything we did was initiated by her. Now that she was helpless, the shack was eerily quiet like a wasted battleground.

This was a colossal disaster for the family, but I was glad for the distraction it provided; I just needed seven days of Aunt's storm falling on this woman, leaving me out. I seemed to be the only one who wasn't surprised at the woman's claims. How right that this happened, and now. Kang-jin deserved this misfortune. It was justice. I hoped that this woman would hold Kang-jin in her death grip, never letting him out of her sight as long as he lived.

• • •

In a matter days, the woman, whose name was Bae-ja, took over our shack. And like a goblin, she popped up everywhere, cleaning everything in sight. In contrast with her slow speech, her movements were nimble and economical. She even took Uncle to the outhouse, washing him at the landlord's water pump and putting clean clothes on him. It seemed that Aunt had found a perfect genie housekeeper, but at what cost.

Still weak, Aunt resigned herself to waiting for her golden son. He would surely take away this humiliating mess. But when In-sook called Kang-jin's tutoring place, Jae-in's fuming uncle said that Kang-jin had better stay away from them and Jae-In. They warned her never to call them again.

So Bae-ja had won, hands down, by letting Aunt kick and hit her until she couldn't stand, and most important of all, by carrying her grandchild. Who could resist a grandson, no matter the circumstances. Bae-ja looked like the kind of woman who'd bear a son right off the bat and have many more. Not an ounce of femininity in her, at nights she snored louder than any of us. What did Kang-jin ever see in her, was what we all thought. But then, whatever did Kang-jin see in me? I knew the answer. It had nothing to do with his feelings but everything to do with his disregard for those less fortunate than the likes of Jae-In. People like Bae-ja and me didn't count.

I was impressed with her and even liked her, but avoided talking to her for fear she might smell me out about Kang-jin and me, or about my leaving. Something told me that no one could bully her. I couldn't see Kang-jin intimidating her; she wouldn't know what that was. If Kang-jin beat her up, she'd think that was what a husband did. And I could easily see her whacking someone with a frying pan, be it Kang-jin or one of her future children. Like Lee, she could cook with what little we had. She had to be an expert at bullying vendors, coming home with extra vegetable here, a bigger piece of mackerel there.

We found out she was a year older than Kang-jin. Despite the years she spent as a housekeeper, she had no "servant" attitude, no bending from her waist for anyone. If she were anyone else, Aunt would have praised her as "a person of a large dish," meaning that she was destined to do big things. But without education and money, that was unlikely; she was a nobody.

I still had four more days to endure. I did my best to keep quiet and inconspicuous. I continued to do my chores to clamp down on the manic jackrabbits jumping around in my stomach. But as Bae-ja took charge, I was running out of chores. So I did what I could when she wasn't looking. Each household item I touched felt like the first and last time, holding a new meaning and intensity. I wouldn't miss this shack or anyone in it, except In-sook, perhaps. Although we had grown apart over the years, I still felt fondness for her.

• • •

The water urn in the kitchen was large, large enough for me to hide in. Into this urn, every morning I added water from the landlord's house. Now Bae-ja did this chore. Because the urn sat tightly between Aunt's shop and the kitchen area with no light, it was hard to clean the inside. Actually we'd never cleaned it since moving here, which made it a perfect home for mould. When we saw little balls of blue mouldy bits floating in it, we simply skimmed them off. But not Bae-ja. She would clean the inner wall of the urn where it was slippery with a slimy film.

I watched with great trepidation as her large torso bent over into the urn. It could just shatter from her weight. Made of clay, these urns were cheap and easily broken. But Bae-ja was skilful. To reach the bottom, she tilted it, even cleaning the unreachable area behind the urn. That was when we heard Aunt gasp, sounding like she saw a ghost, more possibly a rat at her feet. We rushed to her.

There she stood, in the middle of the room, holding a letter, although her legs quickly gave way, collapsing like a folding chair: "What does this mean? *Who's* going to America? It's not possible . . ."

My legs gave way, too. So the Korean government was efficient after all. Things always got twisted, nothing was ever simple. Aunt dropped the letter and grabbed my shoulders, but drained of strength, she let go, crumbling. I caught her and laid her down. She took shallow breaths, her face without colour; she covered her eyes with her arm, shielding them from the light. Bai-ja pulled on the light string.

I didn't mean to harm her; I just wanted to escape quietly. I picked up the immigration notice from the floor. The official letter with red stamp marks at the bottom announced the approval of my immigration, and of my imminent departure, even naming the day and date. Aunt worked to get up. Bae-ja helped her to sit up and brought water to her lips. Aunt shooed her out, and signalled me to stay.

She wanted details. I told her sketchily about Mr. Park and Miss Go, but enough to let her know that people were watching me, and her, too. "You, you betrayed me again. You really did it this time." Her hurt and sadness looked real. Instead of the expected curses, she fell silent.

"Let me ask you. What do you think is waiting for you in America? You think you are going to some beautiful place to live happily? No. Think again. At best, you'll be their housekeeper and a babysitter, then they'll sell you as a slave. That's what's waiting for you there. America is full of stories like that. Your mom? She can barely manage her little kids. She's already gone half crazy. She doesn't need you. Why would she want a grown up girl when she can barely keep up with her young husband? She knows you'll only cause her trouble. That's why she left you here. I swear, she will do it again, she'll throw you away at the first sign of difficulty. Mark my words. And who is this Mr. Park? How can you trust him? How do you know it's really your mom who sent him? What if he's sending you to some slave market. Did you ever think about that?"

I hadn't. I believed Mr. Park. I let her rant, this was her way. At least she was too weak to strike me.

"Your passport and ticket, where are they?"

I told her Mr. Park was holding them.

"You left them with a stranger? Su-young-ah. How can you be so naive? Did you not think that he might run away with them and sell them? Have you any idea how expensive they are?"

I kept mute, but thought—you should know, Aunt, you took that money two years ago.

"We must get them from him before it's too late. Where is he? What's his phone number? We'll call him now." She made a motion to get up.

I said I didn't know how to contact him. I really didn't. Aunt tried to stand up but fell right back. She looked distraught and confused.

"Where's Kang-jin? Go, call him, he should be at his tutoring place. Tell him I need him home. He'll know what to do. Go, now," she said.

I left the shack and took a walk for three blocks to the phone booth and back. It was frightening she didn't remember that Kang-jin no longer tutored and that no one knew where he was. No money would flow from Mom to Aunt anymore. Instead of an heiress, she now had a housekeeper for a daughter-in-law. The end seemed to have come for us all.

• • •

Except for a few school outings, I had never been out of Seoul, never been on a train, let alone on an airplane. And I'd never actually seen the Han River, although it was just below our district and famous for being a suicide destination. My daily life consisted of going around and around Mapo and Jong-ro districts, between home and school, and along the way, churches and the library. The largest body of water I'd seen was in the communal bathhouse. But come Thursday, I would be in the air for a whole day, across the Pacific Ocean, then transported to another world.

If I could, I'd have slept in a cave somewhere, waking up in the plane. Instead, I slept at everyone's feet now that Bae-ja joined us, and I went to school to spend the last days with my classmates, staying away from home. Miss Go didn't seem to mind my diligent daily presence. Now that Aunt knew I was leaving, I had no reason to keep it a secret. Yumi told classmates. And suddenly I became something of a celebrity at school, like out of the Little Princess stories. Classmates who never gave me a thought came to say hello. I was the proverbial unicorn they came to gawk at, envious that I was escaping their gruelling study schedule.

My friends threw a farewell party and gave me a beautifully bound copy of *The Little Prince*, a book we all loved, reading it over and over, taking to heart the author's illustrations of the little prince and his flowing cape, his tiny worlds, and the enchanting little rose that gave him so much trouble, confusion and finally the wisdom. Friends wrote personal farewells and drew small drawings on the corner edges of the pages. Miss Go gave me a Korean/English dictionary. Yumi, a miniature glass bottle filled with earth from her backyard, wrapped in a small Korean flag. I embroidered for her a handkerchief with both of our names.

After school, I walked all the familiar and favourite places—the churches, the public library, the pedestrian bridges, the street market, even the bank on the way home. Yumi and I used to steal into this savings and loan building in hot summer afternoons, the only place where we could count on getting cool air from their mysterious thing called air-conditioning. We'd stand in the lobby, feeling the unnatural, eery chill as if we'd fallen into a deep, cold cave, goose bumps rising on our bare legs and arms. Some mothers thought this air-conditioning was bad for women's childbearing parts. Yumi's mom, whenever she went to the bank, wore a specially made tight underwear so that no poisonous air could affect her.

And for the first time, I went to Yumi's home bearing gifts. Koreans brought gifts whenever they visited someone's home. It was a tradition, a pride. No matter how poor, we brought a token of friendship and gratitude, and we cared about the content, not the wrapping. If you brought an elaborately wrapped box, something even more magnificent had better be inside. Otherwise, it was an insult, and you'd be labelled a cheapskate, a braggart. And you never bragged when you gave a gift, but down played it, so that the recipient wouldn't be underwhelmed when he or she opened it. You'd say, "It's such a nothing, but please accept this humble little thing." I was painfully aware that I had never brought anything to Yumi's family all these years, I only took from them. With the last bit of money I had left, I bought a real Western cake from a bakery, I also gave them my silver-medal-winning watercolour, the one thing I'd love to have taken to America.

Mr. Park fascinated everyone, especially Yumi's younger sister—he was the hero in a thrilling adventure story. Yumi was upset at her slowness: "I should've known! Something was different when you skipped so many classes, so many days in a row. And you paid for coffee and the snack . . ."

Yumi's mom felt bad for Mom: "How hard it must have been for her, leaving you for seven years. My heart breaks thinking about it! What a thing to go through."

Two more nights, just two more nights to go. But it wasn't going to be so simple. When I came home, Aunt was waiting for me, her shop door wide open.

But Aunt didn't look upset, but excited, happy to see me. She even had a bowl of baked potatoes, especially made for me.

When Aunt recovered from her illness, she went on a systematic search for Kang-jin. She didn't succeed, his friends didn't know where he was, Mi-hae didn't come home, sleeping at friends. As daunting as it was, Aunt trekked to Seoul National University looking for him. She didn't get far in the thick maze of its many campuses, her only knowledge was that he was going to be a lawyer. Despite In-sook's report that they barred her from calling them, Aunt called his tutoring place. When they stopped picking up the phone, she took In-sook and went to their home. When they didn't answer her knocking, she picked up a stone to bang on their door, yelling over the wall, demanding they produced Kang-jin, that it was a kidnapping case, that they were being arrogant shits because she was poor. She had made such a ruckus that the police had to be called. She got off with a warning. She also went to Jae-in's hospital, but was rejected at the reception desk.

Then, finally, we received a postcard from Kang-jin: he was going away for a while, needed time, but promised he would clear up this misunderstanding, and everything would be righted again. There was no return address—the real reason why people sent postcards: leave me alone.

This was one drama I'd die to see but I would miss: Kang-jin meeting Bae-ja in front of Aunt.

Aunt led me to her shop, away from the thunder-footed Bae-ja. Her tender touch on my hand surprised me. We lived in such a close proximity that avoiding contact was the polite thing to do, although from time to time I saw her patting In-sook, so pleased at her school report cards.

Aunt had been strangely silent about my going to America. It seemed that with her illness and Kang-jin missing in action, she came to accept my leaving. In-sook said nothing to me either, as if she didn't even know.

"Sit, Su-young-ah, sit here," Aunt offered me her chair, putting herself on the work stool. "I have important news for you. Hear me out. This might change your mind about going to America."

"There she goes again," I thought, "will she never give up?"

"I went to see your father!"

Now, that *was* a stunning piece of news.

"I had to do something. I wasn't going to let you make this huge mistake, running off to America. You know how I feel about your mom and that husband of hers. I don't trust them. So how could I do nothing when your future is at stake."

I knew she'd do anything to keep me. But the news of my father got my attention. It trumped all her other scheming. I knew nothing about him. I sometimes thought that even Mom didn't know who he was, and that I was a result of something terrible that had happened to her. Something like what Kang-jin did, except I got away lucky. But here he was, she had spoken with him, just today.

"We had a long talk, your father and I. We spent all morning together. What nice people! So rich, but so down to earth. And their home! I lost count of how many rooms they had, and a huge garden too, and a car and a driver. Imagine having your own car and a driver!"

She was speaking to me, but her mind seemed to be still with them.

"And you. You are a spitting image of him—even the little habits you have, like smelling first before eating. He smelled the rice cake before he took a bite. A rice cake. Who could possibly smell the difference between two rice cakes?"

I could. But this wasn't the time for that discussion. "Where does he live?" was all I managed to say. I had questions, many, such as why didn't he look for me all these years, wasn't he curious to find out who I was? I was very curious about what he looked like, his personality, what he did, whether he was educated . . .

"He lives right here, in Seoul. He hadn't changed a bit, still such a good looking man, with those piercing eyes. Well, your mom and he were a stunning couple, I give you that. He was ambitious then, but who knew he'd rise up so high, so fast! Owns a big section of Seoul, up northeast side. He had bought up all those crumbling stores and decrepit shacks no one wanted, and rebuilt them all. They took me around in their car. Rows of fancy shops, commercial and residential buildings, street after street, clean paved roads. I am looking at the future of Korea, he said, and by year 2000, we'll be as wealthy a country as America. I don't think that'll ever happen but still . . ."

What a wild idea that I had a father! All this time, one half of me had been blank, like I was lopsided, like I could see through only one eye.

"I had to tell him that you were about to go to America to live with your mom. He didn't know you'd been living with me, that your mom just abandoned you all these years. He got quite upset, for your mom being so irresponsible, for breaking her promise. Well, how could he know, your mom is who she is ... At least she could've talked to him before she left and let you choose: to live with him or with me. But she never did, did she? She hates him, that's why. She didn't want you meeting him, let alone living with him. Why? To punish him, of course. She couldn't bear to give him one thing he loved. Yes, you. How he loved you! After you were born, he was the one who fed you day and night with the bottle while your mom pranced around town wanting to be an actress. What a sight that was: no self-respecting man would do such a thing. He took you everywhere, bundling you up and carrying you on his back like an old nanny. He didn't care people laughed at him. You were everything to him. And your mom couldn't stand it. Sounds crazy, but true. Jealous ... of her own child!

"Well, they were fighting a lot those days, never-ending vicious fights they were, too. The more they fought, the more she kept you away from him. They were not even married. When his parents found out about your mom and you, they were beside themselves. They said *never*. Well, I don't blame them. No respectable family wants an actress for a daughter-in-law. Might as well bring in a harlot. His family was grooming him to be a congressman, like his father. Marriage was out of the question, instead they offered to raise you as theirs, and she could go on being an actress. Your mom said no. Mind you, you weren't her first kid. She was pregnant once before you but it died prematurely. A boy, too. She went crazy for a while. So, in the end, she took away one thing she could from him. You. Now you know the truth."

I felt queasy. My head spun, everything coming at me too quickly.

"Your father came to me many times early on, looking for you. It was that vicious Kyung-hee who told him you were with me."

"Who is Kyung-hee?" I never heard the name before.

"Oh, Mrs. Han, that's who. You know, you lived with her for a very short time. I think your mom went to see you on a day they weren't expecting her, and Kyung-hee was beating you up. For a while, the three of them, Kyung-hee, your mom, and your father—they were as thick as thieves. Anyway, I chased your father away each time. I had to stand by my sister. Eventually he stopped coming around. Then I heard he got married and started his own family. That was about the time when you came to live with me, you must have been five years old or so. I think he gave up being a politician, but obviously he did well in real estate."

So then, the man Mom told me about in her army camp had to be my father. And the earrings she gave me, also from him.

Aunt continued, "You know where you got your
singing talent? Not from my side of the family. From
him, from his beautiful tenor voice. You are through
and through his child, same eyes, nose, the way you
walk, the way you look at people. Who do you think
gave you the name Su-young? Your father. But your
mom kept it from you, making you go on without a
name, till she absolutely had to tell you so you could go
to school. What kind of mother does such a thing to her
own child, I ask you? But that's all water under the
bridge. What's important is you, that's all that matters,
now. He's missed you terribly, wants to make it up to
you. He wants you to live with them, they want to adopt
you. I told them how beautifully you've grown, with all
that talent for singing and painting. His wife, such a
delicate and sweet woman, always wanted to have a
daughter but she can no longer have a child. You're their
God send. And you've got two brothers. What polite
handsome young boys! They are dying to meet you."

Brothers of my own, too. My personal history was
finally beginning to take shape.

"Won't that be much better? Living with your own
father, with your own family? Why go to America
when there's all the luxury and love waiting for you
here? In America, at best, you'll live with your head
down, grateful that they took you in. You think that
skinny bastard will love you like his own flesh and
blood? You can't cheat blood. He will trample you
down. And your mom won't be able to defend you.

What'll you do, where will you go if something bad happened there? Who'll protect you?

"Your mom *had* to go because she had no other choice. But not you. You belong here. You're Korean. Where is your Korean pride? You can live here with your head held high, in your own country, with your own father. Not with a fake one. Don't go. She gave you up to save her ass, and now you want to follow her to a foreign land? It's not like you're going to Japan or China where they at least look like you. No, but to the country of big-nosed, white people, at the opposite end of the world. How are you going to survive? You don't speak their language. It's hard enough to study here. You know that."

That was true. How could I hope to catch up with school studies there? Our one-hour-a-week English classes would be useless in America. I'd be deaf and mute for a long while.

It was maddening. Just as I was getting used to the idea of leaving, my father shows up, offering to change my life right here in Korea. No need to leave school, Yumi or friends. Go on speaking the same language. Never again worry about someone like Madame Daisy. And more than anything, I so wanted to see my father and lift my fifteen years of fog.

"Would it be possible to meet him, tomorrow, then decide?" I asked.

"Of course but not tomorrow. Next week. They left for Japan right after seeing me. I just caught them myself. Everything happened so last minute and all at once. How did I know you were leaving so soon? With me being sick and that crazy woman in our home, it took me a while to track down your father. They couldn't cancel this business trip but promised to cut it short and come back as soon as possible. You'll see them then. Better yet, why not move right in with them? He wants you to spend some time with them anyway. Live with them for a week or two. Then if you still want to go to America, go. You already have the ticket. But once you go, who knows what's waiting for you, it won't be easy to come back. And look, he gave me money—to buy you clothes and whatever you need till you see them." She took out an envelope from her pocket. Koreans always put money in an envelope; it was the polite way.

"At least meet him before you go. You owe him that much. He's your father."

I excused myself for a bathroom break. I needed to think.

"Come back quickly! Don't think too much. I swear, every time people sit down to shit, they change their minds."

Instead of the outhouse, I paced up and down the street, out of sight from Aunt's shop, sorting out my feelings and my mind. They were very conflicted. The very idea of a father was monumental.

If I lived with him, I'd finally have a chance at a normal life. I'd have enough to eat, wear clean clothes and go to school without worrying about tuition. I might get to study piano again and take singing lessons, or even go to that special school for musically talented students. No one would taunt me about being a bastard. What I'd give to see the faces of Kang-jin and Mi-hae when I became a wealthy man's daughter!

But, I couldn't figure out how much of what Aunt said was true and how much made up. Or if any of it were true. What she said about Mom, her separating me and my father, disturbed me. I didn't need to hear that. But then, how could I understand grown up things? And if Aunt knew who my father was, why didn't she tell me sooner? Why wait so long? I wasn't sure if I could ever make the right decision.

Aunt hadn't moved from her stool when I came back.

"Aunt, I like the idea of staying a week or two, then deciding what to do. I really want to meet him. I already have my airline ticket. All I need to do is postpone it. Like you said, once I leave, it won't be easy to come back. Who knows, if I lived with my father, he might even send me to America for my college education, and I could see Mom then. It's just three more years."

"Of course he would send you to America, whenever you want. He'd do anything for you, I know, and he has the means. Su-young-ah, no need to think too hard. I promise you that once you see your father, you'll know you made the right choice."

"Aunt, come Thursday, I'll go and get my passport and ticket from Mr. Park."

"Yes. You go and get them. They are yours. Absolutely!"

Chapter Thirty

"Wait, I'm coming with you," Aunt shouted as I opened the shack door to leave for the airport. She looked sharp in her Sunday dress. I wore the only decent clothes I owned besides my school uniform—a short sleeved beige T-shirt, a pair of blue pants and rubber sandals.

All through the long bus ride to Kimpo airport, we didn't talk, but that wasn't unusual. We didn't chat for chat's sake. Aunt sitting next to me felt as normal and permanent as if she were part of me. I glanced at her spindly body, her thin shoulders, and her bony arms down to her vein-knotted hands—such a fragile body, yet coiled in a ruthless willpower. She worked and struggled harder than anyone I knew, sometimes reminding me of a fish flopping on a butcher's block. I felt a rush of pity; I leaned my head against her shoulder, fighting the urge to cry. She stroked my hair; her forearm smelled familiar and comforting. Leaning on her shoulder, I promised myself: any decision I make from this moment on, I would live with for the rest of my life, without regret, without blame. And when I've turned thirty years old, a very old age indeed—I couldn't imagine living beyond that—I'd say to myself: "You did the right thing, you made the right choice, then," no matter how my life turned out.

We stepped into the airport lobby. I was intimidated by its vast space and worried that I would never find Mr. Park with a crowd of people milling about. I went searching for our designated meeting corner, but instead of Mr. Park, I found Yumi and a half dozen of my friends clustered, holding a banner, "Su-young-ah. Farewell. We Will Miss You!" Yumi was holding a bouquet of flowers. She didn't tell me they were coming. I was moved, but also got nervous. It was not a good thing to have them and Aunt in the same place at the same time.

"Won't they be amazed that you're not leaving," Aunt squeezed my hand. "You did the right thing," she said.

Mr. Park, not far from my friends, was smoking, watching us.

Aunt shot him a look. "Is that him?"

Mr. Park came towards us.

"Hi, you must be Su-young's aunt."

Aunt yanked me to her. Ballooning up, she said,

"And you must be the scammer who seduced my innocent niece. Stay away, you scum-sucking leech! You aren't taking her anywhere. My Su-young is staying. She's going to live with her father. Now hand over her passport and ticket or I'll call the police!"

I was mortified. Here we go again, Aunt's flying off, unable to control herself. My friends circled behind Mr. Park. Strangers gathered around us too. It was an unusual scene—people fighting in an international airport. Mr. Park, for the first time, wore something of a smile. Aunt's temper, now unleashed, was unstoppable.

"You'll go to jail for this, you son of a bitch. You know who Su-young's father is?"

Mr. Park took his time putting out the cigarette under his shoe sole, then slowly looked up.

"Please let go of her arm. She has a plane to catch."

"Go eat shit, you fucking bastard!" Aunt screeched. "Who do you think you are, telling me what to do? Who are you anyway? For all I know, you're scheming to sell my Su-young to somebody, somewhere."

The crowd got thicker at each curse. Yumi was stomping her feet, biting her nails; she knew what Aunt was capable of. Some of my friends giggled at Aunt's expletives. Without a word, Mr. Park pried Aunt's fingers from my arm and pushed her away.

"How dare you!" She hit him with her purse, kicking at him, but Mr. Park deftly sidestepped. Aunt lunged forward and grabbed hold of my arm again.

"Su-young-ah. You tell him. You tell him you aren't going," she said.

Mr. Park let go of my arm.

"Yes, why don't you tell us? Did anything change?" he asked.

I didn't expect this crowd. I didn't expect my friends. And never this fight. I wanted to disappear.

In his usual brusque, non-emotional tone, Mr. Park said, "Are you going to America or staying? I'm good either way."

"Aunt, I am not staying. I'm going to live with my Mom," my voice croaked, shaking inside.

"What do you mean? What about your father? He'll be back next week."

"I'd been thinking. The last two whole days. I'm sorry but I just can't be sure how much of what you said was true."

"What kind of talk is that? Of course it's all true."

"Well, even if all you say is true, it's too late. I can't meet him now. Perhaps later, someday, I'll come back and find him."

"No, you can't do that. You don't know what I had to do to get him. Use your head for once!"

"I'm using my head. It's all so last minute. I was trying to understand why he never came to see me, not in fifteen years. If he loved me so much, why didn't he look for me. Why now? Even now—I thought about this—*he* didn't come looking for me. *You* went to him."

"No, no, no. Can't you see, he's a busy man, an

important man. Now he knows about you and he's ready. You belong with him. Your mom never wanted you. You know that. She's crazy." She shook my shoulders as if to get some sense into me.

Mr. Park tried to interrupt, but I looked at him with a "No." Now was the time. I wanted everything out— the last ten years of bottled-up unsaid things. If it had to be in front of all these people, I couldn't help that.

"Stop saying Mom's crazy," I said, "she's not crazy. I can't stand it when you say that. She didn't do anything crazy. She's the one who kept in touch with you all these years, didn't she? It's you who kept us apart. Now she is sending for me. I'm going. Every single day for the last seven years—two thousand four hundred and fifty-eight days, I missed her! Missed her so much that it hurt, all the time, right here." I was hitting my chest. Saying it out loud broke me. I cried.

Aunt came closer, held my hand. I wrenched it away, stepping back.

"Su-young-ah, think again! I am the one who raised you. Like my own daughter."

"Stop saying that, too. If you did, why didn't you protect me?"

"From what?"

"Kang-jin."

"What do you mean?"

"Bae-ja was no accident. He did the same thing to me." Saying that, I went red, embarrassed to say it in front of my friends and Mr. Park.

"You're lying. That never happened. And Bae-ja won't last. She's gone once Kang-jin comes home. Remember? He said it was all a misunderstanding."

"Why did you hide Mom's letters when you knew how much they meant to me? And you took my Mom's money for years, and never told me!"

"I didn't use it for myself. I was feeding the family and paying the schools. I did my best. We were poor, together."

"No. You used me, Aunt, for your kids. You tried to sell me to a whorehouse." I didn't care anymore if people heard me.

"I don't know what you're talking about. How you go on twisting things! It was for your singing. A chance for you to sing."

"If you sell me to a whorehouse, it's not to sing! Do I want to meet my father? Yes, very much. But not this way. Not with you standing between me and him. Not with you holding a knife to my throat."

"I don't know what you are babbling about. I'm giving you a chance to live with that great man and you're letting it go, just to spite me? I swear, if you leave now, I'll never tell you who he is, or how to find him."

"I know you won't. Still I can't stay. Because, even if he was for real, you would play him for all his worth. You'll hold me hostage and make him pay. I won't be your bank any more. If I stay, you'll suck me dry until I die."

I turned and signalled to Mr. Park that I was ready.

"You ungrateful bitch, how dare you talk to me that way!" She swung at me, but Mr. Park caught her fist in mid-air. He nodded, looking past Aunt. Two airport policemen appeared out of nowhere, they called him, sir, and held Aunt back. All the while, the crowd grew.

"No, no. That's the man you want to arrest, not me. He's kidnapping my niece!" Aunt yelled. Seeing they weren't listening to her, she shouted into the thick crowd. "Please, somebody help! He's taking my child!" Aunt writhed in their hold.

Mr. Park said, "You'll only get hurt. Let her go, Su-young-aunt. Stop carrying on like this. This is an international airport. Let's not embarrass ourselves in front of the foreigners."

But Aunt wasn't done. "You are *not* my kid. That's right. You are just a bastard your stupid bitch mom dropped like a hot rock. And if Kang-jin did what you say, you deserved it. You're nothing. To educate my children, I'd do far worse than use you."

"I know, Aunt. Lying is nothing for you. So for once, I lied right back about me not going to America. Like you, I'd do anything, anything to get away from you and Kang-jin. I want to be with Mom even if, as you say, she is crazy."

She spat right at me, it landed at my feet.

"Get out. You are no good to me. I hope that plane crashes!"

People gasped, pointing at me and Aunt, shaking their heads, talking among themselves.

Mr. Park took my arm and led me towards the plane. "You're going to do well in America," he said.

Yumi and friends swamped around me, their eyes glowing as if they just came out of a movie. Yumi rushed forward, handed me the flowers and a bundle of presents she kept for me, then engulfed me into her arms. We held each other until Mr. Park patted my back, urging me to move on.

Before getting on the plane, he gave me the passport, ticket, and a piece of paper with Mom's address and phone number. I bowed to him. I turned around one last time. People were still gathered around Aunt, who was sprawled on the floor, face in hands, wailing.

I knew I'd made the right choice, no matter what.

● ● ●

A kindly stewardess guided me to my seat next to a window and gently put the seatbelt around me.

The plane took off and from high above, I finally saw the Han River in its entirety.

The word "Han" is very particular to Koreans—we are people full of sadness, bitterness, and with deep aches in our souls. The best known meaning of "Han" is "the beauty of sorrow." How apt it was that as I was soaring away from the Han River, my sorrow was never beautiful.

Soon the Han River flowed to her great mother, the Yellow Sea. I, too, was flowing to my mother, leaving behind all that was me, then.